Official Journal of the 'Mediterranean League against Thromboembolic Diseases'

Pathophysiology of Haemostasis and Thrombosis

Formerly 'Haemostasis'

KARGER

Printed in Switzerland on acid-free paper by Reinhardt Druck, Basel

Appears bimonthly: 1 volume per year (6 issues)

Guidelines for Authors

Pathophysiology of Haemostasis and Thrombosis

Submission

Only original papers written in English that communicate novel findings in the field of haemostasis and thrombosis are considered. Both contributions to the basic understanding of these processes and reports on clinical management of disorders in this field are acceptable. Manuscripts should be sent to:

Editorial Office
'Pathophysiology of Haemostasis and Thrombosis'
attn. Mrs. T. Camphuisen-Engel
Maastricht University
Department of Biochemistry
Faculty of Medicine II, Level 4
P.O. Box 616
NL–6200 MD Maastricht (The Netherlands)
Tel. +31 43 388 1678/1674
Fax +31 43 388 4159
E-Mail T.Camphuisen@bioch.unimaas.nl

Manuscripts should be submitted in triplicate (with three sets of illustrations of which one is an original), typewritten double-spaced on one side of the paper, with a wide margin.

Conditions

All manuscripts are subject to editorial review. A manuscript is to be considered rejected when an author does not return a revised manuscript within 3 months of receiving the suggestions for revision, unless the author explains further delay. Manuscripts are received with the explicit understanding that they are not under simultaneous consideration by any other publication. Submission of an article for publication implies the transfer of the copyright from the author to the publisher upon acceptance. Accepted papers become the permanent property of 'Pathophysiology of Haemostasis and Thrombosis' and may not be reproduced by any means, in whole or in part, without the written consent of both the author and the publisher. It is the author's responsibility to obtain permission to reproduce illustrations, tables, etc. from other publications.

Arrangement

Title page: The first page of each paper should indicate the title, the authors' names, and the institute where the work was conducted. A short title for use as running head as well as the full address of the author to whom correspondence should be sent are also required.

Full address: The exact postal address complete with postal code must be given at the bottom of the title page. Please also supply phone and fax numbers, as well as your e-mail address.

Key words: For indexing purposes, a list of 3–10 key words in English is essential.

Abstract: Each paper needs an abstract of up to 10 lines.

Footnotes: Avoid footnotes. When essential, they are numbered consecutively and typed at the foot of the appropriate page.

Tables and illustrations: Tables and illustrations (both numbered in Arabic numerals) should be prepared on separate sheets. Tables require a heading and figures a legend, also prepared on a separate sheet. For the reproduction of illustrations, only good drawings and original photographs can be accepted; negatives or photocopies cannot be used. Due to technical reasons, figures with a screen background should not be submitted. When possible, group several illustrations on one block for reproduction (max. size 181 × 223 mm) or provide crop marks. On the back of each illustration, indicate its number, the author's name, and 'top' with a soft pencil.

Color illustrations: Up to 6 color illustrations per page can be integrated within the text at the reduced price of CHF 660.– / USD 545.00 per page. Color illustrations are reproduced at the author's expense.

References: In the text identify references by Arabic numerals [in square brackets]. Material submitted for publication but not yet accepted should be noted as 'unpublished data' and not be included in the reference list. The list of references should include only those publications which are cited in the text. Do not alphabetize; number references in the order in which they are first mentioned in the text. The surnames of the authors followed by initials should be given. There should be no punctuation other than a comma to separate the authors. Cite all authors, 'et al' is not sufficient. Abbreviate journal names according to the Index Medicus system. (Also see International Committee of Medical Journal Editors: Uniform requirements for manuscripts submitted to biomedical journals. N Engl J Med 1997;336:309–315.)

(a) Papers published in periodicals: Sun J, Koto H, Chung KF: Interaction of ozone and allergen challenges on bronchial responsiveness and inflammation in sensitised guinea pigs. Int Arch Allergy Immunol 1997;112:191–195.
(b) Monographs: Matthews DE, Farewell VT: Using and Understanding Medical Statistics, ed 3, revised. Basel, Karger, 1996.
(c) Edited books: Parren PWHI, Burton DR: Antibodies against HIV-1 from phage display libraries: Mapping of an immune response and progress towards antiviral immunotherapy; in Capra JD (ed): Antibody Engineering. Chem Immunol. Basel, Karger, 1997, vol 65, pp 18–56.

Page charges

There are no page charges for papers of 4 or fewer printed pages (including tables, illustrations and references). Each additional complete or partial page is charged to the author at CHF 275.– / USD 196.00. The allotted size of a paper is equal to approx. 12 manuscript pages (including tables, illustrations and references).

Galley proofs

Unless indicated otherwise, galley proofs are sent to the first-named author and should be returned with the least possible delay. Alterations made in galley proofs, other than the correction of printer's errors, are charged to the author. No page proofs are supplied.

Reprints

Order forms and a price list are sent with the galley proofs. Orders submitted after the issue is printed are subject to considerably higher prices.

KARGER

Fax +41 61 306 12 34
E-Mail karger@karger.ch
www.karger.com

The Guidelines for Authors are available at:
www.karger.com/journals/pht/pht_gl.htm

General Information

Pathophysiology of Haemostasis and Thrombosis

Publication data: 'Pathophysiology of Haemostasis and Thrombosis' is published 6 times a year. Volume 32 with 6 issues appears in 2002.

Subscription rates: Subscriptions run for a full calendar year. Prices are given per volume.
Personal subscription:
Subscription + postage and handling
CHF 439.– + CHF 28.80 Europe
CHF 439.– + CHF 42.70 Overseas
USD 337.50 + USD 28.80
+ online subscription per volume:
CHF 39.– / USD 30.00
(Must be in the name of, billed to, and paid by an individual. Order must be marked 'personal subscription'.)
Institutional subscription:
Subscription + postage and handling
CHF 878.– + CHF 36.– Europe
CHF 878.– + CHF 53.40 Overseas
USD 675.00 + USD 36.00
+ online subscription per volume:
CHF 58.– / USD 45.00
Airmail postage: CHF 36.–, USD 30.00.
(Extra per volume.)
Discount subscription prices:
Gesellschaft für Thrombose- und Haemostase-Forschung;
International Society of Haematology.

Microforms: Please direct all enquiries and orders to:
University Microfilms Inc.
300 North Zeeb Road, P.O. Box 1346
Ann Arbor, MI 48106-1346 (USA)

Subscription orders: Orders can be placed at agencies, bookstores, directly with the
Publisher S. Karger AG, P.O. Box,
CH–4009 Basel (Switzerland)
or with any of the following distributors:
Deutschland: S. Karger GmbH, Postfach
D–79095 Freiburg
France: Librairie Luginbühl
36, bd de Latour-Maubourg
F–75007 Paris
Great Britain, Ireland: S. Karger AG
4 Rickett Street
London SW6 1RU, UK
USA: S. Karger Publishers, Inc.
26 West Avon Road, P.O. Box 529
Farmington, CT 06085, USA
India, Bangladesh, Sri Lanka:
Panther Publishers Private Ltd.
33, First Main
Koramangala First Block
Bangalore 560 034, India
Japan: Karger Japan, Inc.
Yushima S Bld. 3F
4-2-3, Yushima, Bunkyo-ku
Tokyo 113-0034, Japan

Change of address: Both old and new address should be sent to the subscription source.

Single issues and back volumes: Information can be obtained through the Publisher.

Advertising: Correspondence and rate requests should be addressed to the Publisher.

Bibliographic indices: This journal is regularly listed in bibliographic services, including *Medline/PubMed.*

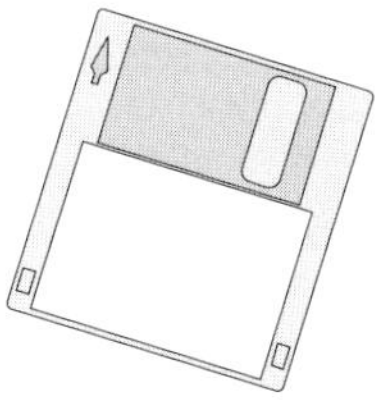

Disk Submission

A **comprehensive version** of these guidelines for the **submission of manuscripts and illustrations on disk** can be accessed online under **www.karger.com/journals/disksub.htm** or requested as a leaflet from the editorial department.

Please follow the general rules on style and arrangement in the **'Guidelines for Authors'** of the journal. Submit a **double-spaced printout** of your manuscript matching the file on disk exactly.

Technical Information

Store only data pertinent to this manuscript. Include your fonts (screen and printer fonts for Macintosh). For a **text only** manuscript, use a 3.5-inch disk. For **text and illustrations,** use 3.5 or 5.25 Magneto Optical Disc; CD-ROM (DOS or hybrid); iomage Zip/DOS (100 MB), or 44 MB, 88 MB or 200 MB SyQuest. Compress extensive data using ZIP format.

Data Description

Label your disk with the **title of the journal or book** for which it is submitted; a **short version** of the paper's title; your **name,** postal and e-mail address, fax and phone number; **hard- and software** used, including the version; and the **complete list of the file names.** File names consist of eight characters before the dot identifying the file and three characters after the dot identifying the application.

Text and Format

The **preferred word-processing package is MS-Word.** Other commonly used PC text programs and ASCII formats are accepted.
Update your data when you revise subsequent to the reviewer's or editor's decision and mark revisions clearly. Manuscripts accepted for publication are subject to **copy editing:** changes and/or questions will be marked in the manuscript, which will be returned to you with your disk and the galley proofs for checking.
Enter your text continuously flush left. Do not use any layout functions. Do not split words at the end of a line. **Do not use indentations.** Use a blank line before and a hard return at the end of paragraphs.
Arrange headings flush left. Insert only **one space after punctuation marks.** Insert Greek letters, mathematical symbols etc. with your word-processing program. Use **boldface and italics** as well as sub- and superscript where appropriate.
Tables are part of the text and should be placed at the end of the text file. Separate the individual parts of a table by lines. Use the tabulator instead of spaces. Format operation data on one line in the same column. **Legends to illustrations are part of the text** and should also be listed at the end of the text file.

Illustrations

Store illustrations as separate files: do not integrate them in your text. Export **line drawings/vector graphics** as TIF, EPS or WMF format. Use Photoshop for processing and retouching **scanned halftone images.** Save the original scan and the processed version. Export **black and white or color images** as TIF or EPS format in their anticipated size in print.
For detailed information on how to submit illustration data on disk please consult the leaflet or **www.karger.com/journals/disksub.htm.**

KI 98 DISK

KARGER

Fax + 41 61 306 12 34
E-Mail karger@karger.ch
www.karger.com

The Guidelines for Authors are available at:
www.karger.com/pht

Pathophysiology
of Haemostasis
and Thrombosis

Clinical Management of Thrombotic and Cardiovascular Disorders with Thrombin Inhibitors: The Role of Argatroban

Satellite Symposium held at the International Society of Thrombosis and Haemostasis, July 11, 2001, Paris

Guest Editors

Hans K. Breddin, Frankfurt/Main
Jeanine M. Walenga, Maywood, Ill.

41 figures, 8 in color, 10 tables, 2002

KARGER

Basel · Freiburg · Paris · London · New York ·
Bangalore · Bangkok · Singapore · Tokyo · Sydney

Supported by an educational grant from Mitsubishi Pharma Corporation

S. Karger
Medical and Scientific Publishers
Basel · Freiburg · Paris · London
New York · Bangalore · Bangkok
Singapore · Tokyo · Sydney

Drug Dosage
The authors and the publisher have exerted every effort to ensure that drug selection and dosage set forth in this text are in accord with current recommendations and practice at the time of publication. However, in view of ongoing research, changes in government regulations, and the constant flow of information relating to drug therapy and drug reactions, the reader is urged to check the package insert for each drug for any change in indications and dosage and for added warnings and precautions. This is particularly important when the recommended agent is a new and/or infrequently employed drug.

Printed in Switzerland on acid-free paper by
Reinhardt Druck, Basel
ISBN 3–8055–7558–0

KARGER

Fax + 41 61 306 12 34
E-Mail karger@karger.ch
www.karger.com

Vol. 32, Suppl. 3, 2002

Pathophysiology of Haemostasis and Thrombosis

Contents

KARGER

Fax + 41 61 306 12 34
E-Mail karger@karger.ch
www.karger.com

Access to full text and tables of contents, including tentative ones for forthcoming issues: www.karger.com/pht_issues

Pathophysiology of Haemostasis and Thrombosis

Pathophysiol Haemost Thromb 2002;32(suppl 3):1–8
DOI: 10.1159/000069102

Current Developments in Antithrombotic Therapy: The Role of Antithrombin Agents

H.K. Breddin

International Institute of Thrombosis and Vascular Diseases e.V., Frankfurt, Germany

Key Words
Thrombin inhibitors · Hirudin · Hirulog · PEG-hirudin · Argatroban · Inogatran · Melagatran · Heparin-induced thrombocytopenia

Abstract
Hirudin, the specific thrombin inhibitor from medicinal leeches, is now produced by recombinant technology. r-Hirudin and to a lesser extent polyethyleneglycol-coupled hirudin (PEG-hirudin) have been used in many clinical trials. Hirudin has been shown to be more effective than low molecular weight heparin in the prevention of deep venous thrombosis after total hip replacement. In (acute) coronary syndromes hirudin as well as a synthetic hirudin analogue bivalirudin have been studied in large clinical trials. Higher doses of hirudin were associated with an increased risk of bleeding. A large-scale study with bivalirudin in patients with acute MI (the HERO-2 trial) has not shown a reduction in mortality but a 30% reduction of reinfarction within 96 h. Hirudin and argatroban have been successfully used in patients with heparin-induced thrombocytopenia type II. Several orally active thrombin inhibitors are being developed. The combined use of subcutaneous and oral administration of melagatran in patients with hip or knee replacement has led to promising results. It is likely that in the future thrombin inhibitors will replace other forms of anticoagulation in a number of indications.

Introduction

During the last 20 years, low molecular weight heparins have replaced unfractionated heparin (UFH) in many indications. UFH has a similar effect on thrombin and the coagulation factor Xa, but heparins are not direct inhibitors of thrombin and factor Xa. They activate the plasma proteins antithrombin and heparin co-factor II, and this mechanism leads to their anticoagulant effects. Heparins have been used for 40 years in the prophylaxis and treatment of venous or arterial thromboses; improvements in therapy may be anticipated from direct thrombin or factor Xa inhibitors. Specific thrombin inhibitors are independent of the plasma level of antithrombin and of the inactivation of thrombin by heparin cofactor II.

Thrombin plays a central role in regulating thrombotic processes. It is a glycosylated, trypsin-like proteinase, which is formed out of prothrombin by the prothrombinase complex (factors Xa, Va, calcium and phospholipids).

Thrombin influences the permeability of platelet membranes, it has direct effects on the vascular endothelium and many other actions on different cell systems, including the stimulation of synthesis and release of mediators from vascular endothelium. After the characterization of the first specific thrombin inhibitor hirudin by Fritz Markwardt, many other thrombin inhibitors have been detected in different haematophagus animals [1]. Today hirudin is produced by recombinant technology

KARGER
Fax +41 61 306 12 34
E-Mail karger@karger.ch
www.karger.com

Accessible online at:
www.karger.com/pht

Prof. Dr. H.K. Breddin
International Institute of Thrombosis and Vascular Diseases e.V.
Ferdinand-Schrey-Weg 6
D–60598 Frankfurt am Main (Germany)
Tel. +49 69 637964, Fax +49 69 63152220, E-Mail Breddin@em.uni-frankfurt.de

and new inhibitors are synthetized. Low molecular weight thrombin inhibitors have been developed later on.

Hirudin and other thrombin inhibitors have been studied in a number of clinical trials and at present several oral thrombin inhibitors are being developed by different pharmaceutical companies.

Parenteral Thrombin Inhibitors

Hirudin

Hirudin is a specific thrombin inhibitor which was originally obtained from the salivary glands of the medicinal leech *(Hirudo medicinalis)*. It was first isolated and characterized by Markwardt [2] in 1957. For approximately 20 years, hirudin has been produced by recombinant technology (r-hirudin). r-Hirudins are as active and specific as natural hirudin. r-Hirudin and a polyethyleneglycol-coupled hirudin (PEG-hirudin) have been investigated in clinical trials in different indications. Hirudin and r-hirudin have a molecular weight of 7,000 D. The molecular weight of PEG-hirudin is 17,000 D. Hirudin-derived molecules, such as hirulog, have been used in different clinical trials [3, 4].

Methods for the Monitoring of Hirudin and Other Thrombin Inhibitors

The measurement of the thrombin-inhibiting effect (anti-F-IIa-activity) in plasma using a chromogenic substrate is probably the most precise method to monitor prophylaxis or treatment with hirudin. However, the ecarin time is simpler, more practical and especially suited for bedside monitoring [5, 6]. The ecarin clotting time (ECT) is well correlated with the inhibition of thrombin as it is measured using chromogenic substrates. Other methods including the activated partial thromboplastin time (aPTT) and the activated clotting time (ACT) can also be used to monitor the effect of thrombin inhibitors. These methods, however, are not specific and are modified by acquired and inborn coagulation defects and in addition they are not well standardized. The thrombin time is too sensitive and therefore less suited for the control of thrombin inhibitors [7].

Hirudin in Coronary Heart Disease

Large clinical trials with r-hirudin in patients with unstable angina [8], patients with acute myocardial infarctions or acute coronary syndromes [9–13] and after coronary angioplasty [14] have been published.

In the two largest studies (GUSTO 2a and TIMI 9a), a relatively high initial intravenous bolus of 0.6 mg/kg hirudin was followed by a continuous infusion of 0.2 mg/kg/h [9, 12]. All patients received aspirin and many were also treated with thrombolytic agents. Both studies were stopped because of increased intracranial bleedings, and in the GUSTO 2a study increased mortality had been observed in the hirudin arms. In the TIMI 9a study, there were 14% major bleedings in the hirudin group compared to 10% in the heparin group.

Both studies were restarted with a much lower initial intravenous bolus of 0.1 mg/kg followed by an intravenous infusion 0.1 mg/kg/h. Following this change, bleeding complications under hirudin were not more frequent than in the heparin group. The clinical efficacy was equivalent to or minimally better than that of heparin [15, 16].

In further studies [17–19], another recombinant hirudin (HBW 023) was used in patients with acute myocardial infarcts together with streptokinase. The patients received either hirudin (i.v. bolus of 0.2 mg/kg, followed by 0.5 mg/kg/h as continuous infusion) or UFH. There were no significant differences in either efficacy or bleeding complications between the two treatment groups. It is possible that the observed hemorrhagic complications in the studies with higher hirudin doses were partially caused by the concomitant use of aspirin.

Interactions of Hirudin and Aspirin

We compared the effect of PEG-hirudin and aspirin alone with a combination of PEG-hirudin and aspirin in healthy volunteers [20]. A mean hirudin level of 1.8 μg/ml was achieved. The bleeding time was minimally prolonged under PEG-hirudin, slightly prolonged under aspirin but very much prolonged in volunteers who received 300 mg aspirin + PEG-hirudin. The effect of the combination was more than additive. We cannot yet explain what causes this synergistic effect of a combination of hirudin and aspirin.

Similar interaction studies with heparin and aspirin have shown that the combined use leads to prolongation of the bleeding time but only to a slight additive effect [21].

Hirudin in the Prophylaxis and Treatment of Deep Venous Thrombosis

Hirudin has been more effective than UFH in the prophylaxis of thrombosis after total hip replacement [22]. In another large study [23], recombinant hirudin (2 × 15 mg/day s.c.) was compared with the low molecular weight heparin enoxaparin (once daily 40 mg s.c.). Enoxaparin was administered to 1,023 patients and hirudin to 1,028 patients. The thrombosis rate in the enoxaprin group was 28.5% and 18.4% in the hirudin group; hirudin reduced the incidence of proximal thrombosis (7.5% in the enoxaparin group, 4.5% in the hirudin group). The difference was statistically significant. r-Hirudin was more effective than low molecular weight heparin in this high-risk population. Hirudin has been approved for this indication.

There are few data on the treatment of acute deep venous thrombosis with hirudin [24, 25]. In this indication, low molecular weight heparins probably are more suitable, and their effect has been established in many clinical trials. Moreover, at higher doses hirudin probably needs laboratory monitoring.

Possible Further Development of Hirudin and PEG-Hirudin

r-Hirudin and PEG-hirudin are being investigated in new trials in patients with unstable angina. It is expected that PEG-hirudin, because of its longer half-life, will reduce the amount of hirudin needed and will also lead to more stable plasma levels.

In patients with renal insufficiency there is a risk of overdosing because the elimination of hirudin is considerably impaired.

Hirudin can be used instead of UFH in cardiopulmonary bypass. Many cardiac surgeons are concerned about heparin-induced thrombocytopenia (HIT) in patients who have had prior heparin exposure. This risk does not exist with hirudin and in some centers hirudin is successfully used instead of UFH for the anticoagulation in combination with extracorporeal circulation.

Bivalirudin

Bivalirudin (hirulog) was compared with UFH in several studies in patients undergoing PTCA in acute coronary syndromes and has shown increased efficacy and reduced bleeding risk in both indications [3, 26–31]. Bivalirudin at a dose of 1 mg/kg every 8 h was effective in a dose-finding study on the prevention of thromboses after major hip or knee surgery [32].

In a recent study (HERO acute MI study) bivalirudin, given as an intravenous bolus of 0.2 mg/kg, followed by 0.5 mg/kg/h for 12 h and 0.2 mg/kg/h up to 60 h, led to an increased TIMI grade 3 coronary flow in a higher percentage of patients and to a reduced incidence of death, MI and cardiogenic shock compared to UFH [33].

In the large HERO 2 trial in 17,000 patients with acute MI bivalirudin has been compared with UFH [33]. Bivalirudin did not reduce mortality compared with UFH but reduced reinfarction by 30% within 96 h. There was a slight increase in mild and moderate bleeding in patients treated with bivalirudin.

Argatroban

Argatroban is a synthetic direct thrombin inhibitor derived from *L*-arginine and was initially developed by Mitsubishi Chemical Industries. In Japan, the drug is approved for Buerger's disease, arteriosclerosis obliterans, acute cerebral thrombosis and anticoagulation of antithrombin-III-deficient patients undergoing hemodialysis. The use of argatroban in Japan will be discussed later in this issue.

Argatroban is excreted through the liver and therefore does not accumulate in renally impaired patients. Argatroban can be monitored using aPTT. Argatroban is a less potent inhibitor of thrombin than lepirudin, but this fact is associated with a (probably) larger therapeutic window. Argatroban will not produce antibodies and therefore long-term and repeat treatments are possible. Argatroban can easily be monitored [34].

Preliminary studies have shown successful use of argatroban for anticoagulation during percutaneous coronary intervention in HIT II-patients without excessive bleeding [35–40].

Inogatran

Inogatran is a low molecular weight specific thrombin inhibitor that has been investigated in patients with myocardial ischemia (TRIM study). In this study, inogatran was administered intravenously; no advantage in comparison to UFH could be demonstrated [41]. After stopping the inogatran infusion, a reactivation of thrombin and increased ischaemic reactions have been described [42]. The concomitant use of inogatran and aspirin did not lead to potentiation of anticoagulant effects [43].

Orally Active Thrombin Inhibitors

Melagatran (Ximelagatran)

H376/95, the prodrug of melagatran, is a small molecule (molecular weight 474 D) with a bioavailability of about 20%. The molecule is absorbed within 15–30 min, the highest melagatran plasma levels are reached within 1–2 h.

In the METHRO II-study melagatran (24 mg) was compared with dalteparin in 1,876 patients with total knee or hip replacement. In both patient groups, melagatran was significantly more effective than dalteparin. The thrombosis incidence was almost halved in patients with total hip replacement or total knee replacement [44, 45]. Melagatran is presently being investigated in several further large clinical trials. One of the most interesting questions is whether thrombin inhibitors will be more effective or as effective as vitamin K antagonists with less bleeding complications.

Thrombin Inhibitors in the Treatment of Heparin-Induced Thrombocytopenia

Heparin-induced thrombocytopenia is observed in some patients during the first days of heparin treatment. Their platelet count normalizes after a few days under continued heparin administration. This phenomenon is not antibody related. It also has been named HIT type I (HIT I) or heparin-associated thrombocytopenia type I (HAT I).

Heparin-induced thrombocytopenia type II (HIT II) is triggered by an immune response to heparin. HIT II with thrombotic complications is frequently named HITT or HITTS. However, many authors use the expression 'HIT' for all types of heparin-induced thrombocytopenia with and without thrombotic complications.

For the diagnosis of HIT II, a reduction of platelet count, especially during days 3–21 after onset of heparin treatment, and clinical symptoms are more important than laboratory tests. The frequency of HIT II in different patient groups is not well established. Frequencies of 2–5% of all heparin-treated patients have been described [46–48], but in prospective trials on the treatment of deep venous thrombosis and also in patients undergoing vascular surgery lower percentages have been reported [49–52].

HIT II has been observed in medically and surgically treated adults, during pregnancy and in newborns [53, 54]. The most dramatic and dangerous clinical complications of HIT II are venous and/or arterial thromboses. Patients with HIT-II-associated thrombosis have been reported to have a mortality of 25–30% and an amputation rate of up to 25% [54].

The pathophysiological process of HIT II is associated with the generation of antibodies which bind to a complex of heparin coupled with peptides and proteins on platelet and endothelial cell surfaces [55–62]. The currently accepted hypothesis of the pathophysiology of HIT II is based on the development of an IgG antibody to the heparin-PF4 complex that also recognizes the FcγRIIA receptor on platelets. Binding of this complex causes platelet aggregation and thrombin generation. This concept is probably incomplete because the interactions between endothelium and antibodies are still not fully understood. The antibodies are not heparin specific and have been shown to react with low molecular weight heparins and dermatans [63, 64]. Endothelial cells are probably involved in the mechanism via binding of the antibody to glycosaminoglycans on the cell surface [57, 61, 62] but also to other endothelial epitopes. Damaged endothelial cells probably are the starting point for thrombotic complications.

Heterogeneity of HIT II Patients

Patients with HIT II show a large variation of clinical and laboratory symptoms. They may have a fall in platelet count with a positive antibody test with a very good prognosis if heparin is discontinued.

Patients with thrombotic complications may have been treated with heparin for several reasons. They may have already existing thrombosis, they may have a fresh thrombotic complication and the diagnosis of HIT II may have been made after several thrombotic complications in a late stage with a very poor prognosis. In addition, prognosis also depends on underlying diseases. Because of this wide variation, general statements on mortality are misleading.

'Prophylaxis'

If heparin-induced thrombocytopenia type II is suspected based on a fall in platelet count which cannot be otherwise explained and before clinical symptoms appear, heparin should immediately be discontinued and a prophylactic treatment against high-risk thrombosis should be started. There is no consensus as to the optimum prophylactic regimen to prevent imminent thromboses. Early discontinuation of heparin alone does not affect the thrombotic event rate, although early recognition may improve mortality [54]. But since early discontinuation of heparin treatment and an early switch to alternative anticoagulation are likely to prevent thrombotic complications and to reduce mortality, this kind of prophylaxis is clearly recommended.

General Management

Patients with HIT II and documented clinical thrombosis have a clear indication for anticoagulation and should be treated with danaparoid (Orgaran®) or a thrombin inhibitor monitored to obtain therapeutic aPTT levels. A coumarin-derivative may be initiated if the thrombin inhibitor has been given for 4–7 days. Small doses of the vitamin K antagonist should be used initially and the thrombin inhibition should be continued until therapeutic levels of the vitamin K antagonist are documented [38, 64, 65]. Among other treatment modalities, two anticoagulants are used in Europe: Orgaran and the thrombin inhibitor hirudin (lepirudin). In addition, argatroban has been released in the US for this indication.

For prophylactic treatment of HIT II patients, a thrombin inhibitor can be initiated with low level of anticoagulation until the thrombocytopenia resolves [34].

Hirudin

Hirudin (lepirudin, Refludan®) has been approved for the treatment of thrombosis in patients with HIT II in the USA and Germany. Hirudin does not cross-react with heparin antibodies as shown by in vitro data and successful treatment of HIT II patients [66–68]. Two multi-center trials on lepirudin have been published and have demonstrated a statistically significant reduction in the primary efficacy endpoint assessed by an overall composite index (new thrombosis, amputation and death) [69, 70] in comparison with historic controls. Results on lepirudin treatment in HIT II patients have also been published recently [71, 72].

There are problems with hirudin treatment. Because the drug is renally excreted, hirudin accumulates in patients with renal insufficiency, a dose reduction is often necessary and monitoring with dose modifications becomes difficult [73, 74].

Another issue is the production of lepirudin-specific antibodies. Around 40% of patients develop antibodies against the drug. Furthermore, an investigation of data from two prospective multicenter studies of lepirudin in HIT type II patients revealed that the anticoagulant effect of lepirudin was enhanced in about 45% of the patients in whom such antibodies were detected [75]. In an investigation of anti-hirudin antibody isotypes in 23 patients with HIT type II treated with lepirudin, 13 patients (56%) developed anti-hirudin antibodies of at least one isotype [75].

In conclusion, the potential for an antibody response complicates the management of the anticoagulant activity of lepirudin.

Argatroban

Argatroban was approved in June 2000 in the US for the prophylaxis and treatment of thromboses in patients with HIT type II. Efficacy and safety in this indication were demonstrated, in one historically controlled pivotal study and one new follow-on supportive study [39].

Orgaran

The low molecular weight heparinoid (danaparoid) Orgaran is a mixture of nonheparin polysulfated glycosaminoglycans (heparan sulfate, dermatan sulfate, chondroitin sulfate, low molecular weight heparin). Similar to heparin in structure, danaparoid differs from heparin in its degree of sulfation and molecular weight.

In vitro studies using HIT-II-positive sera showed a cross-reaction in 18 versus 100% for heparin [34]. Danaparoid has been approved for the prophylaxis of thrombosis after hip replacement surgery. It was used for many years off-label for anticoagulation in HIT II-patients [76–79] but is now approved for the treatment of HIT II-patients in Europe. Disadvantages of danaparoid are difficulties in monitoring, lack of well-established dosing guidelines [80], possibly increased postoperative bleeding [81] and the possibility of cross-reactions leading to a symptomatology similar to HIT II [78].

References

1 Markwardt F: Coagulation inhibitors from animals feeding on blood. Rev Ibero Amer Thromb Hemost 1994;7:225–231.
2 Markwardt F: Die Isolierung und chemische Charakterisierung des Hirudins. Hoppe-Seyler's Z Physiol Chem 1957;308:147–156.
3 Fox I, Dawson A, Loynds P, Eisner J, Findlen K, Lenn E, Hanson D, Mant T, Wagner J, Maraganore J: Anticoagulant activity of hirulog, a direct thrombin inhibitor in humans. Thromb Haemost 1993;69:157–163.
4 Maraganore JM, Bourdon P, Jablonski J, Ramachandran L, Fenton JW: Design and characterization of hirulogs: A novel class of bivalent peptide inhibitors of thrombin. Biochemistry 1990;29:7095–7101.
5 Nowak G, Bucha E: Quantitative determination of hirudin in blood and body fluids. Semin Thromb Haemost 1996;22:197–202.
6 Pötzsch B, Madlener K, Seelig C, Riess CF, Greinacher A, Müller-Berghaus G: Monitoring of r-hirudin anticoagulation during cardiopulmonary bypass – assessment of the whole blood ecarin clotting time. Thromb Haemost 1997; 77:920–925.
7 Schenk JF, Glusa E, Radziwon P, Markwardt F, Breddin HK: A recombinant hirudin (IK-HIR02) in healthy volunteers. I. Effects on coagulation parameters and bleeding time. Haemostasis 1996;26:140–149.

8 Van den Bos A, Deckers JW, Heyndrickx GR, Laarman GJ, Suryapranata H, Zijlstra F, Close P, Rijnierse JMM, Buller HR, Serruys PW: Safety and efficacy of recombinant hirudin (CGP 39 393) versus heparin in patients with stable angina undergoing coronary angioplasty. Circulation 1993;88:2058–2066.
9 Antman EM for the TIMI 9A investigators: Hirudin in acute myocardial infarction: Safety report from the thrombolysis and thrombin inhibition in myocardial infarction (TIMI) 9A trial. Circulation 1994;90:1624–1630.
10 Cannon CP, McCabe CH, Henry TD, Schweiger MC, Gibson RS, Mueller HS, Becker RC, Kleiman NS, Haugland M, Anderson JL, Sharaf BL, Edwards SJ, Rogers WJ, Williams DO, Braunwald E: A pilot trial of recombinant desulfatohirudin compared with heparin in conjunction with tissue type plasminogen activator and aspirin for acute myocardial infarction: Results of the thrombolysis in myocardial infarction (TIMI) 5 trial. J Am Coll Cardiol 1994, 23:993–1003.
11 Lidon RM, Théroux P, Lesperance J, Adelman B, Bonan R, Duval, D, Levesque J: A pilot, early angiographic patency study using a direct thrombin inhibitor as adjunctive therapy to streptokinase in acute myocardial infarction. Circulation 1994;89:1567–1572.
12 The Global Use of Strategies to Open Occluded Coronary Arteries (GUSTO) IIa-investigators. Randomized trial of intravenous heparin versus recombinant hirudin for acute coronary syndromes. Circulation 1994;90:1631–1637.
13 Organisation to Assess Strategies for Ischemic Syndromes (OASIS-2) Investigators: Effects of recombinant hirudin (lepirudin) compared with heparin on death, myocardial infarction, refractory angina, and revascularisation procedures in patients with acute myocardial ischaemia without ST elevation: A randomised trial. Lancet 1999;353:429–438.
14 Herrman JPR; Simon R, Umans VAWM, Peerboom PF, Keane D, Runierse JJMM, Bach D, Kobi P, Kerry R, Close P, Deckers JW, Serruys PW: Evaluation of recombinant hirudin (CGP 39 393/registered REVASC) in the prevention of restenosis after percutaneous transluminal coronary angioplasty. Rationale and design of the Helvetica trial, a multicentre randomized double blind heparin controlled study. Eur Heart J 1995;16:56–62.
15 Antman EM for the TIMI 9B investigators: Hirudin in acute myocardial infarction. Thrombolysis and thrombin inhibition in myocardial infarction (TIMI) 9B trial. Circulation 1996;94:911–921.
16 The Global Use of Strategies to Open Occluded Coronary Arteries (GUSTO) II-investigators: A comparison of recombinant hirudin with heparin for the treatment of acute coronary syndromes. N Engl J Med 1996;335:775–782.
17 Neuhaus KL, von Essen R, Tebbe U, Jessel A, Heinrichs H, Mäurer W, Döring W, Harmjanz D, Kötter V, Kalhammer E, Simon H, Horacek T: Safety observations from the pilot phase of the randomized r-hirudin for improvement of thrombolysis (HIT-III) study. A study of the Arbeitsgemeinschaft Leitender Kardiologischer Krankenhausärzte (ALKK). Circulation 1994;90:1638–1642.
18 Neuhaus KL, Moloek GP, Zeymer U, Tebbe U, Wegscheider K, Schroder R, Camez A, Laarman GJ, Grollier GM, Lok DJ, Kuckuck H, Lazarus P: Recombinant hirudin (lepirudin) for the improvement of thrombolysis with streptokinase in patients with acute myocardial infarction: Results of the HIT-4 trial. J Am Coll Cardiol 1999;34:966–973.
19 Von Essen R, Zeymer U, Tebbe U, Jessel A, Kwasny H, Mateblowski M, Niederer W, Wagner J, Maurer W, von Leitner ER, Haerten K, Roth M, Neuhaus KL: HBW 023 (recombinant hirudin) for the acceleration of thrombolysis and prevention of coronary reocclusion in acute myocardial infarction: Results of a dose-finding study (HIT-II) by the Arbeitsgemeinschaft Leitender Kardiologischer Krankenhausärzte. Coron Artery Dis 1998;9:265–272.
20 Breddin HK, Radziwon P, Eschenfelder V, Müller-Peltzer H, Esslinger HU: PEG-hirudin and acetylsalicylic acid show a strong interaction on bleeding time. Ann Haematol 1996; 72(suppl I):A 53.
21 Bang CJ, Riedel B, Talstad I, Berstad A: Interaction between heparin and acetylsalicylic acid on gastric mucosal and skin bleeding in humans. Scand J Gastroenterol 1992;27:489–494.
22 Eriksson BI, Ekman S, Kälebo P, Zachrisson B, Bach D, Close P: Prevention of deep-vein thrombosis after total hip replacement: Direct thrombin inhibition with recombinant hirudin, CGP 39393. Lancet 1996;347:635–639.
23 Eriksson BI, Joergensen PW, Kälebo P, Mouret P, Rosencher N, Bösch P, Baur M, Ekman S, Bach D, Linbratt S, Close P: A comparison of recombinant Hirudin with a low molecular weight heparin top prevent thromboembolic complications after total hip replacement. N Engl J Med 1997;337:1329–1335.
24 Parent F, Bridey F, Dreyfus M, Musset D, Grimon G, Duroux P, Meyer D, Simoneau G: Treatment of severe venous thromboembolism with intravenous hirudin (HBW 023): An open pilot study. Thromb Haemost 1993;70:386–388.
25 Schiele F, Vuillemenot A, Kramarz P, Kieffer Y, Soria J, Soria C, Camez A, Mirshahi MC, Bassand JP: A pilot study of subcutaneous recombinant hirudin (HBW 023) in the treatment of deep vein thrombosis. Thromb Haemost 1994;71:558–562.
26 Kong DF, Topol EJ, Bittl JA, White HD, Theroux P, Hasselblad V, Califf RM: Clinical outcomes of bivalirudin for ischemic heart disease. Circulation 1999;100:2049–2053.
27 Maraganore JM, Bourdon P, Jablonski J, Ramachandran L, Fenton JW: Design and characterization of hirulogs: A novel class of bivalent peptide inhibitors of thrombin. Biochemistry 1990;29:7095–7101.
28 Piana RN, Ahmed WH, Chaitman B, Ganz P, Kinlay S, Strony J, Adelman B, Bittl JA: Effect of transient abrupt vessel closure during otherwise successful angioplasty for unstable angina on clinical outcome at six months. Hirulog Angioplasty Study Investigators. J Am Coll Cardiol 1999;33:73–78.
29 Théroux P, Pérez-Villa F, Waters D, Lespérance J, Shabani F, Bonan R: Randomized couble-blind comparison of two doses of hirulog with heparin as adjunctive therapy to streptokinase to promote early patency of the infarct-related artery in acute myocardial infarction. Circulation 1995;91:2132–2139.
30 Topol EJ, Bonan R, Jewitt D, Sigwart U, Kakkar VV, Rothman M, de Bono D, Ferguson J, Willerson JT, Strony J, Ganz P, Cohen MD, Raymond R, Fox I, Maraganore J, Adelman B: Use of a direct antithrombin, hirulog, in place of heparin during coronary angioplasty. Circulation 1993;87:1622–1629.
31 Sharma GVRK, Lapsley DE, Vita JA, Sharma S, Coccio E, Adelman B, Loscalzo J: Safety and efficacy of hirulog in patients with unstable angina. Circulation 1992;86:I-386.
32 Ginsberg JS, Nurmohamed MT, Gent M, MacKinnon B, Sicurella J, Brill-Edwards P, Levine MN, Panju AA, Powers P, Stevens P, Turpie AGG, Weitz J, Buller HR, ten Cate JW, Neemeh J, Adelman B, Fox I, Maraganore J, Hirsh J: Use of hirulog in the prevention of venous thrombosis after major hip or knee surgery. Circulation 1994;90:2385–2389.
33 White H: The Hirulog and Early Reperfusion or Occlusion (HERO)-2 Trial Investigators. Thrombin-specific anticoagulation with bivalirudin versus heparin in patients receiving fibrinolytic therapy for acute myocardial infarction: The HERO-2 randomised trial. Lancet 2001; 358:1988–1963.
34 Walenga JM, Fasanella AR, Iqbal O, Hoppensteadt DA, Ahmad S, Wallis DE, et al: Coagulation laboratory testing in patients treated with argatroban. Semin Thromb Hemost 1999; 25(suppl 1):61–66.
35 Lewis BE, Ferguson JJ, Grassman ED, Fareed J, Walenga JM, Joffroin JL, et al: Successful coronary intervention performed with argatroban anticoagulation in patients with heparin-induced thrombocytopenia and thrombosis syndrome. J Invas Cardiol 1996;8:410–417.
36 Lewis BE, Iaffaldano R, McKiernan TL, Rao L, Donkin J, Walenga JM: Report of successful use of argatroban as an alternative anticoagulant during coronary stent implantation in a patient with heparin-induced thrombocytopenia and thrombosis syndrome. Cathet Cardiovasc Diagn 1996;38:206–209.

37 Lewis BE, Rangel Y, Fareed J: The first report of successful carotid stent implant using argatroban anticoagulation in a patient with heparin-induced thrombocytopenia and thrombosis syndrome. A case report. Angiology 1998;49:61–67.
38 Lewis BE, Walenga JM, Wallis DE: Anticoagulation with Novastan® (argatroban) in patients with heparin-induced thrombocytopenia and thrombosis syndrome. Semin Thromb Hemost 1997;23:197–202.
39 Lewis BE, Wallis DE, Berkowitz SD, Matthai WH, Fareed J, Walenga JM, et al: Argatroban anticoagulant therapy in patients with heparin-induced thrombocytopenia. Circulation 2001;103:1838–1843.
40 Suzuki S, Sakamoto S, Koide M, Matsuo M, Fuji K, Matsuo T: Effective anticoagulation by argatroban during coronary stent implantation in a patient with heparin-induced thrombocytopenia. Thromb Res 1997;88:499–502.
41 Thrombin inhibition in myocardial ischaemia (TRIM) study group: A low molecular weight, selective thrombin inhibitor, inogatran, vs. heparin in unstable coronary artery disease in 1209 patients. A double-blind, randomized, dose-finding study. Eur Heart J 1997;18:1416–1425.
42 Andersen K, Dellborg M, Emanuelsson H, Grip L, Swedberg K: Thrombin inhibition with inogatran for unstable angina pectoris: Evidence for reactivated ischaemia after cessation of short-term treatment. Coron Artery Dis 1996;7:673–681.
43 Chen LY, Nichols WW, Mattsson C, Teger-Nilson AC, Wallin R, Saldeen TG, Mehta JL: Aspirin does not potentiate effect of suboptimal dose of the thrombin inhibitor inogatran during coronary thrombolysis. Cardiovasc Res 1995;30:866–874.
44 Eriksson BI, Ögren M, Agnelli G, Cohen A, Dahl OE, Mouret P, Rosencher N, Eskilson C, Nylander I, Frison L: The oral direct thrombin inhibitor ximelagatran (pINN, formerly H 376/95) and its subcutaneous form melagatran compared with enoxaparin as thromboprophylaxis after total hip or total knee replacement. Thromb Haemost 2001;suppl:abstract OC1638.
45 Gustafsson D, Nystrom J, Carlsson S. Bredberg U, Eriksson U, Gyzander E, Elg M, Antonsson T, Hoffmann K, Ungell A, Sorensen H, Nagard S. Abrahamsson A, Bylund R: The direct thrombin inhibitor melagatran and its oral prodrug H 376/95: Intestinal absorption properties, biochemical and pharmacodynamic effects. Thromb Res 2001;101:171–181.
46 Aster RH: Heparin-induced thrombocytopenia and thrombosis. N Engl M Med 1995;332:1374–1376.
47 Warkentin TE: Venous thromboembolism in heparin-induced thrombocytopenia. Curr Opin Pulm Med 2000;6:343–351.
48 Warkentin TE, Levine MN, Hirsh J, Horsewood P, Roberts RS, Gent M, Kelton JG: Heparin-induced thrombocytopenia in patients treated with low-molecular-weight heparin of unfractionated heparin. N Engl J Med 1995;332:1330–1335.
49 Harenberg J, Schmidt JA, Koppenhagen K, Tolle A, Huisman MV, Büller HR: Fixed-dose, body weight-independent subcutaneous LMW heparin versus adjusted dose unfractionated intravenous heparin in the initial treatment of proximal venous thrombosis. Thromb Haemost 2000;83:652–656.
50 Kirchmaier CM, Wolf H, Schäfer H, Ehlers B, Breddin HK: Efficacy of a low molecular weight heparin administered intravenously or subcutaneously in comparison with intravenous unfractionated heparin in the treatment of deep venous thrombosis. Int Angiol 1998;17:135–145.
51 Lindhoff-Last E, Eichler P, Stein M, Plagemann J, Gerdsen F, Wagner R, Ehrly AM, Bauersachs R: A prospective study on the incidence and clinical relevance of heparin-induced antibodies in patients after vascular surgery. Thromb Res 2000;97:387–393.
52 Lindhoff-Last E, Nakov R, Mosch G, Breddin HK, Bauersachs R: Incidence and clinical relevance of heparin-PF4-antibodies in 1137 patients with deep venous thrombosis treated with UFH or LMWH. Ann Hematol 2000;79(suppl I):A3.
53 Greinacher A, Eckhardt T, Mussmann J, Mueller-Eckhardt C: Pregnancy complicated by heparin associated thrombocytopenia management by a prospective in vitro selected heparinoid (ORG 10172). Thromb Res 1993;71:123–126.
54 Wallis DE, Workman DL, Lewis BE, Steen L, Pifarré R: Failure of early heparin cessation as treatment for heparin-induced thrombocytopenia. Am J Med 1999;106:629–635.
55 Amiral J, Bridey, F, Dreyfus M, Vissoc AM, Fressinaud E, Wolf M, et al: Platelet factor 4 complexed to heparin is the target for antibodies generated in heparin-induced thrombocytopenia. Thromb Haemost 1992;68:95–96.
56 Brandt JT, Isenhart CE, Osborne JM, Ahmed A, Anderson CL: On the role of platelet FcγRIIA phenotype in heparin-induced thrombocytopenia. Thromb Haemost 1995;74:1564–1572.
57 Cines DB, Tomaski A, Tannenbaum S: Immune endothelial-cell injury in heparin associated thrombocytopenia. N Engl J Med 1987;316:581–589.
58 Greinacher A, Michels I, Liebenhoff U, Presek P, Mueller-Eckhardt C: Heparin-associated thrombocytopenia: Immune complexes are attached to the platelet membrane by the negative charge of highly sulphated oligosaccharides. Br J Haematol 1993;84:711–716.
59 Greinacher A, Pötzsch B, Amiral J, Dummel V, Eichner A, Mueller-Eckhardt C: Heparin-associated thrombocytopenia: Isolation of the antibody and characterization of a multimolecular PF-4 heparin complex as the major antigen. Thromb Haemost 1994;71:247–251.
60 Kelton JG, Smith JW, Warkentin TE, Hayward CPM, Denomm GA, Horsewood P: Immunoglobulin G from patients with heparin-induced thrombocytopenia binds to a complex of heparin and platelet factor 4. Blood 1994;83:3232–3239.
61 Visentin GP, Ford SE, Scott JP, Aster RH: Antibodies from patients with heparin-induced thrombocytopenia/thrombosis are specific for platelet factor 4 complexed with heparin or bound to endothelial cells. J Clin Invest 1994;93:81–88.
62 Warkentin TE, Hayward CP, Boshkov LK, Santos AV, Sheppard JI, Bode AP, Kelton JG: Sera from patients with heparin-induced thrombocytopenia generate platelet derived microparticles with procoagulant activity: An explanation for the thrombotic complications of heparin-induced thrombocytopenia. Blood 1994;84:3691–3699.
63 Greinacher A, Feigl M, Mueller-Eckhardt C: Crossreactivitiy studies between sera of patients with heparin-associated thrombocytopenia and a new low molecular weight heparin, reviparin. Thromb Haemost 1994;72:644–645.
64 Walenga JM, Lewis BE, Hoppensteadt DA, Fareed J, Bakhos M: Management of heparin-induced thrombocytopenia and heparin-induced thrombocytopenia and thrombosis syndrome. Clin Appl Thromb Hemost 1997;3(suppl 1):53–63.
65 Wallis DE, Quintos R, Wehrmacher W, Messmore H: Safety of warfarin anticoagulation in patients with heparin-induced thrombocytopenia. Chest 1999;116:1333–1338.
66 Olbrich K, Wiersbitzky M, Wacke W, Eichler P, Zinke H, Schwock M, Mox B, Kraatz G, Motz W, Greinacher A: Atypical heparin-induced thrombocytopenia complicated by intracardiac thrombus, effectively treated with ultra-low-dose rt-PA lysis and recombinant hirudin (lepirudin). Blood Coagul Fibrinolysis 1998;9:273–277.
67 Walenga JM, Jeske WP, Wallis DE, Bakhos M, Lewis BE, Leya F, et al: Clinical experience with combined treatment of thrombin inhibitors and GP IIb/IIIa-inhibitors in patients with HIT. Semin Thromb Hemost 1999;25(suppl 1):77–81.
68 Walenga JM, Lewis BE, Jeske WP, Leya F, Wallis DE, Bakhos M, et al: Combined thrombin and platelet inhibition treatment for HIT patients. Hämostaseologie 1999;19:128–133.
69 Greinacher A, Eichler P, Lubenow N, Kwasny H, Luz M: Heparin-induced thrombocytopenia with thromboembolic complications: Meta-analysis of 2 prospective trials to assess the value of parenteral treatment with lepirudin and its therapeutic aPTT range. Blood 2000;96:846–851.
70 Greinacher A, Janssens U, Berg G, Kwasny H, Kemkes-Matthes B, Eichler P, Volpel H, Potzsch B, Luz M: Lepirudin (recombinant hirudin) for parenteral anticoagulation in patients with heparin-induced thrombocytopenia. Heparin-Associated Thrombocytopenia Study (HAT) investigators. Circulation 1999;100:587–593.
71 Schneider T, Heuer B, Deller A, Boesken WH: Continuous haemofiltration with r-hirudin (lepirudin) as anticoagulant in a patient with heparin induced thrombocytopenia (HIT II). Wien Klin Wochenschr 2000;112:552–555.

72 Shah AC, Genoni M, Neiderhauser U, Maloigne M, Turina M: R-hirudin (lepirudin, refludan) as an alternative anticoagulant in heparin-induced thrombocytopenia during cardiopulmonary bypass connection. Schweiz Med Wochenschr 2000;130:896–899.
73 Davenport A: Management of heparin-induced thrombocytopenia during continuous renal replacement therapy. Am J Kidney Dis 1998;32: E3.
74 Fisher KG, van de Loo A, Bohler J: Recombinant hirudin (lepirudin) as anticoagulant in intensive care patients treated with continuous hemodialysis. Kidney Int 1999;56(suppl 72): S46–50.
75 Eichler P, Friesen HJ, Lubenow N, Jaeger B, Greinacher A: Antihirudin antibodies in patients with heparin-induced thrombocytopenia treated with lepirudin: Incidence, effects on aPTT, and clinical relevance. Blood 2000;96: 2373–2378.
76 Gillis S, Merin G, Zahger D, Deeb M, Drenger B, Hyam E, Eldor A: Danaparoid for cardiopulmonary bypass in patients with previous heparin-induced thrombocytopenia. Br J Haematol 1997;98:657–659.
77 Gitlin SD, Deeb GM, Yann C, Schmaier AH: Intraoperative monitoring of danaparoid sodium anticoagulation during cardiovascular operations. J Vasc Surg 1998;27:568–575.
78 Magnani HN: Heparin-induced thrombocytopenia (HIT): An overview on 230 patients treated with orgaran (Org 10172). Thromb Haemost 1993;70:554–561.
79 Magnani HN: Einsatz von Danaparoid (Orgaran®) zur Antikoagulation bei kardiovaskulären Operationen. VASA 2000;29(suppl 56): D02.
80 Brieger DB, Mak KH, Kottke-Marchant K, Topol EJ: Heparin-induced thrombocytopenia. J Amer Coll Cardiol 1998;31:1449–1459.
81 Chong BH, Ismail F, Cade J, Gallus AS, Gordon S, Chesterman CN: Heparin-induced thrombocytopenia: Studies with a new low molecular weight heparinoid, Org 10172. Blood 1989;73:1592–1596.

Pathophysiology of Haemostasis and Thrombosis

Pathophysiol Haemost Thromb 2002;32(suppl 3):9–14
DOI: 10.1159/000069103

An Overview of the Direct Thrombin Inhibitor Argatroban

Jeanine M. Walenga

Thoracic and Cardiovascular Surgery and Pathology, Loyola University Medical Center, Maywood, Ill., USA

Key Words

Argatroban · Thrombin inhibitor · Anticoagulant

Abstract

Argatroban is a small molecule direct thrombin inhibitor. The main attributes of this synthetic drug are its rapid onset of anti-thrombin action, rapid reversibility of its anticoagulant effect, potent inhibition of clot-bound thrombin, absence of antibody formation and no need for initial dosage adjustment in patients with renal impairment. It is eliminated by hepatic metabolism. These properties make argatroban a predictable anticoagulant with intravenous use in a routine clinical setting. Argatroban is approved in the US and Canada for both prophylaxis and treatment of thrombosis in patients with heparin-induced thrombocytopenia (HIT); and it is approved in Japan and Korea for treatment of various thrombotic disorders. Argatroban has been shown in limited trials to provide reliable anticoagulation during percutaneous coronary interventions on HIT and non-HIT patients. Preliminary reports document the feasibility of using argatroban for anticoagulation during peripheral vascular interventions, hemodialysis and as adjunct to thrombolysis for treatment of myocardial infarction. Current recommendations for argatroban monitoring are to use the activated partial thromboplastin time for low doses and the activated clotting time for high doses. The ease of monitoring argatroban, its 'turn-on/turn-off' characteristic and its consistent safety profile provide the rationale to continue studies of argatroban as an anticoagulant in clinical settings.

Introduction

Argatroban is a direct thrombin inhibitor that was discovered in the 1970s by Shosuke Okamoto in Japan [1, 2]. Many preclinical as well as pilot clinical studies have been performed and published on argatroban [3, 4].

Argatroban was first clinically used in Japan in patients for treatment of peripheral arterial occlusive disease in the early 1980s. Today it is approved in Japan for treatment of arterial thrombosis (1990), acute cerebral thrombosis (1996) and anticoagulation of AT-deficient patients undergoing hemodialysis (1996). Argatroban is also approved in Korea for use in chronic arterial occlusion and acute cerebral thrombosis. Argatroban was approved in the United States in 2000 for both prophylaxis and treatment of thrombosis associated with heparin-induced thrombocytopenia (HIT) type II. In Canada,

KARGER

Fax +41 61 306 12 34
E-Mail karger@karger.ch
www.karger.com

1424–8832/02/0329–0009$18.50/0

Accessible online at:
www.karger.com/pht

Jeanine M. Walenga, PhD
Cardiovascular Institute, Loyola University Medical Center
2160 S. First Ave.
Maywood, IL 60153 (USA)
Tel. +1 708 327 2838, Fax +1 708 327 2849, E-Mail jwaleng@lumc.edu

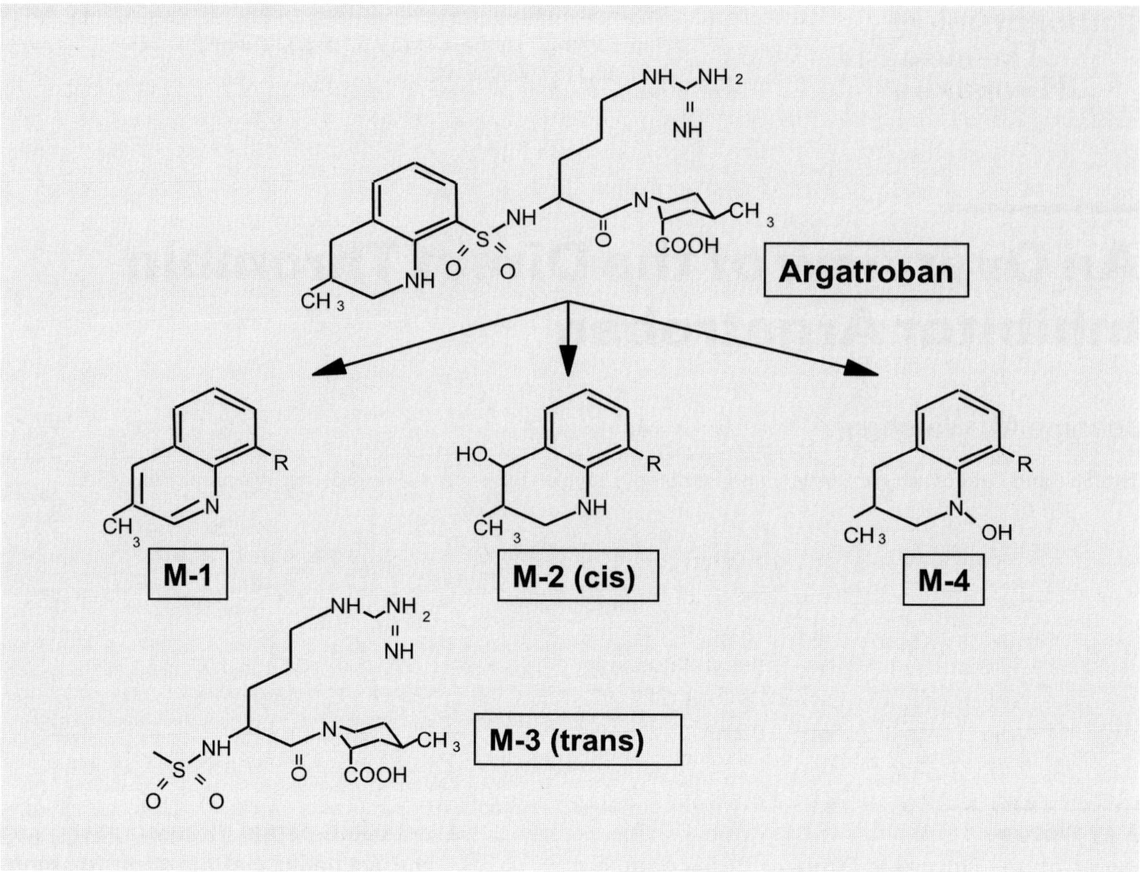

Fig. 1. The structure of the direct thrombin inhibitor argatroban and its four major metabolites.

argatroban is approved as an anticoagulant for HIT patients who, in the opinion of the attending physician, require anticoagulation. A submission to the European health authorities for use of argatroban in patients with HIT type II is in progress.

Pharmacologic Profile of Argatroban

Mechanism of Action

Argatroban is a synthetic small molecule derived from *L*-arginine with a molecular weight of 527 D (fig. 1) [5, 6]. Its mechanism of action is direct thrombin inhibition through a reversible interaction with the catalytic site of thrombin [7–9]. The thrombin inhibition constant (K_i) of argatroban is 3.9×10^{-8} *M*. It is a selective thrombin inhibitor and does not inhibit other serine proteases. Approximately 54% is bound to plasma proteins [10].

The small molecular size of argatroban may offer a therapeutic advantage for treatment of older, more organized thrombi, in that it can penetrate and effectively inhibit thrombin despite the fibrin barrier [11–13]. It has been demonstrated that a 2-fold increase in concentration is needed to penetrate and neutralize fibrin-bound thrombin in vitro or in vivo (vs. inhibition of soluble fibrin) for argatroban. This is compared to a 23-fold (in vitro) or 4,000-fold (in vivo) increase needed for hirudin and a 500-fold (in vitro) or 5,000-fold (in vivo) increase for heparin in the same model systems.

Pharmacokinetics

Argatroban reaches its steady-state plasma levels, measured by its activated partial thromboplastin time (aPTT) anticoagulant effect, 1–3 h after initiation of intravenous administration (faster when a loading bolus is administered) [14, 15]. Low intra- and intersubject variability is observed. Plasma drug concentrations increase proportionally with doses up to 40 μg/kg/min and are well correlated with steady-state anticoagulant effects. The dose-response curve is gentle and predictable, allowing for a wide margin of safety during dose titration. After discontinuation of the drug, aPTT returns to normal within 2–4 h. Its elimination half-life is 39–51 min, and is unaffected by age, gender and renal function [16].

Patients with moderate hepatic impairment, compared with healthy volunteers, have an approximate 4-fold decrease in drug clearance (to 1.5 ml/min/kg) and an approximate 3-fold increase in elimination half-life (to 152 min) [17]. Owing to the decreased clearance, a 4-fold downward adjustment in argatroban dosage is required for individuals with moderate hepatic impairment.

Metabolism

Argatroban is rapidly metabolized in the liver and excreted through the bile into the feces [14, 15, 17, 18]. There are three known metabolites of argatroban (M1, M2 and M3) (fig. 1). M1 retains a very modest antithrombin effect [19]. The anticoagulant effect of M1 is not clinically apparent with routine intravenous dosing.

Argatroban does not induce the formation of antibodies that neutralize its anticoagulant effect, prolong its half-life or enhance its activity [20].

Antidote

No specific antidote is available for argatroban. If life-threatening bleeding occurs and excessive plasma argatroban levels are suspected, argatroban should be discontinued immediately, and the patient provided symptomatic and supportive therapy. Anticoagulant parameters generally return to baseline within 2–4 h after argatroban discontinuation [14, 15]. This reversal may take at least 6 h and perhaps more than 20 h in hepatically impaired patients [17].

Drug Interactions

There have been no pharmacokinetic or pharmacodynamic drug interactions reported between argatroban and aspirin, erythromycin, acetaminophen, digoxin, or lidocaine [21–23]. In practice, argatroban co-administered with these frequently used medications should require no dosage adjustments.

Warfarin/Argatroban Combined Therapy

Because argatroban is a direct thrombin inhibitor, concurrent use of argatroban and warfarin prolongs the prothrombin time (PT)/International Normalized Ratio (INR) beyond that produced by warfarin alone [24]. Hence, the previously established ('traditional') relationship between the INR and bleeding is altered. In general, with doses of argatroban up to 2 μg/kg/min, argatroban can be discontinued when the INR is >4 on combined therapy [25]. The level of warfarin can be checked 4–6 h after discontinuing argatroban when its effect is negligible. For argatroban doses >2 μg/kg/min the relationship is less predictable. In this case, the argatroban infusion can be temporarily reduced to 2 μg/kg/min, and the INR repeated on argatroban and warfarin 4–6 h after argatroban reduction.

Concurrent use of argatroban and warfarin, compared with warfarin monotherapy, exerts no additional effect on vitamin-K-dependent factor levels [26]. However, because the measurement of coagulation factors by clot-based assays will be affected by argatroban, immunologic or chromogenic-based assays should be used [24].

Monitoring

The anticoagulant effects of argatroban are routinely monitored using the aPTT [24]. Higher levels of anticoagulation such as required during interventional procedures are monitored using the activated clotting time (ACT) [15, 24, 27]. Argatroban also increases the thrombin time and ecarin clotting time (ECT) in a dose-dependent fashion [24].

Clinical Studies of Argatroban

HIT/HITTS (ARG-911)

Patients with HIT have an allergy to heparin and are at high risk of developing life- and limb-threatening thrombosis. Traditionally, warfarin, dextran and aspirin, for lack of better drug options, have been used to anticoagulate these patients. With the availability of direct thrombin inhibitors that have potent anticoagulant activity, the concept of utilizing this drug class to treat patients with HIT was developed. From the ARG-911 multi-center clinical trial, argatroban therapy, at a starting dose of 2 μg/kg/min adjusted to achieve an aPTT of 1.5–3 times the baseline value, has been shown to produce significant benefits in the clinical outcomes of patients with isolated HIT or HIT with thrombosis, compared with historical controls [28]. Argatroban therapy effectively reduced the composite of death, amputation or new thrombosis, lowered mortality from thrombosis, and prevented new thrombotic events. These favorable outcomes were achieved without an increase in bleeding, relative to control, and with no patient experiencing intracranial hemorrhage while on argatroban therapy. In addition, patients re-exposed to argatroban at another clinical treatment had equally favorable outcomes [29].

Percutaneous Coronary Intervention

In patients with HIT requiring percutaneous coronary intervention (PCI), aggressive anticoagulation is needed to avoid thrombosis. The hypercoagulable state characterizing HIT together with the endovascular disruption resulting from PCI may place HIT patients at particular risk of thrombosis during PCI. In a pilot study and subsequent clinical trials of argatroban (ARG-216, ARG-310/311), primary efficacy assessments showed satisfactory outcome of the procedure and adequate anticoagulation of patients undergoing their initial PCI with argatroban [27, 30]. No unsatisfactory outcomes occurred during repeat PCIs with argatroban.

The use of argatroban in patients without HIT has been studied in the setting of PCI. In three pilot studies, procedural success was reported [31–33]. A multi-center clinical trial in North America on the use of argatroban anticoagulation for non-HIT patients undergoing PCI is nearly completed, and results will be available in early 2003.

Case reports have also described the successful use of argatroban anticoagulation in patients with HIT during carotid and renal stent implants [34, 35]. Argatroban dosing was similar to that for coronary interventional procedures. Argatroban has shown an acceptable safety and tolerability profile in these patients.

Stroke

In Japan, argatroban is used for the treatment of acute cerebral thrombosis [36]. A preliminary multi-center clinical trial in North America to establish the safety and explore the efficacy of argatroban as a treatment for acute ischemic stroke is nearly complete. Results will be available in early 2003.

Other Thrombotic States

Anticoagulation with argatroban has been evaluated in acute myocardial infarction, unstable angina, peripheral arterial obstructive disease and as an adjunct to thrombolytic therapy [37–40]. In each of these settings, argatroban produced predictable anticoagulant effects and was generally safe and well tolerated.

A few cases describing the successful use of argatroban anticoagulation during hemodialysis in HIT patients have been reported [41, 42]. No relevant differences were shown, compared with patients who did not require hemodialysis, in major bleeding or the composite end-point of death, amputation or new thrombosis over 37 days.

Argatroban versus Other Antithrombotic Drugs

Heparins and Coumadin Derivatives

Argatroban offers several advantages over the traditional anticoagulants heparin and warfarin. In comparison to heparin, argatroban is a selective, direct inhibitor of thrombin that is not dependent on AT or other cofactors. It is a more potent inhibitor of bound thrombin than heparin or low molecular weight heparins, and the mechanism of action of argatroban is less complex than that of warfarin. Warfarin can be associated with limb gangrene when used in patients with HIT. Argatroban does not cross-react with the heparin antibody in patients with HIT as do low molecular weight heparins and to a lesser extent danaparoid.

Other Direct Thrombin Inhibitors

Two other thrombin inhibitors, lepirudin (Refludan®) and hirulog (Angiomax®), have received approval in the US. These drugs are pharmacologically distinct from argatroban and exhibit different safety/efficacy profiles. Argatroban has a rapid onset of action and is rapidly reversed following discontinuation. This characteristic provides a wider safety net than that of the less quickly reversed hirudin (or danaparoid).

Hirudin is a protein and thus generates antibodies that increase its anticoagulant activity by prolonging the half-life or antibodies that decrease its anticoagulant effect by neutralizing the drug [43]. Because it is of similar structure as hirudin, hirulog may also generate antibodies. Immunogenicity to argatroban has not been reported [20].

Argatroban is cleared through the liver not the kidney, and thus it can be used in patients with kidney disease with no adjustment of starting dose. In contrast, hirudin is cleared through the kidneys and patients with renal impairment require dose reduction to avoid excess plasma concentrations.

The thrombin inhibitors have varying effects on the traditional clotting assays. The aPTT and ACT can typically be used for monitoring depending on the dose of the drug. Because argatroban has a linear dose-dependent effect on these assays, they can be used with confidence for dose adjustment minimizing the bleeding risk.

Summary

The introduction of thrombin inhibitor drugs, such as argatroban, has added a new dimension to the management of thrombosis. These drugs offer a unique substitute for anticoagulation in patients who are heparin compromised, an option we have not had prior to now. Argatroban appears to be a safe, easy to dose drug, with consistent response between individuals. Current clinical trials of argatroban are focusing on its expanded use in stroke and other thrombotic disorders.

References

1 Okamoto S, Hijikata A: Potent inhibition of thrombin by the newly synthesized arginine derivative No. 805. The importance of stereostructure of its hydrophobic carboxamide portion. Biochem Biophys Res Commun 1981; 101:440–446.

2 Okamoto S, Hijikata-Okunomiya A: Synthetic selective inhibitors of thrombin. Methods Enzymol 1993;222:328–340.

3 Hursting MJ, Alford KL, Becker JC, Brooks RL, Joffrion JL, Knappenberger GD, Kogan PW, Kogan TP, McKinney AA, Schwarz RP: Novastan (brand of argatroban): A small-molecule, direct thrombin inhibitor. Semin Thromb Hemost 1997;23:503–516.

4 Jeske W, Walenga JM, Lewis BE, Fareed J: Pharmacology of argatroban. Exp Opin Invest Drugs 1999;8:625–654.

5 Bush LR: Argatroban, a selective, potent thrombin inhibitor. Cardiovasc Drug Rev 1991;9:247–263.

6 Hijikata-Okunomiya A, Okamoto S: A strategy for a rational approach to designing synthetic selective inhibitors. Semin Thromb Hemost 1992;18:135–149.

7 Kikumoto R, Tamao Y, Tezuka T, Tonomura S, Hara H, Ninomiya K, Hijikata A, Okomoto S: Selective inhibition of thrombin by (2*R*, 4*R*)-4-methyl-1-[N^2-[(3-methyl-1,2,3,4-tetrahydro-8-quinolinyl)sulfonyl]-*L*-arginyl)]-2-piperidinecarboxylic acid. Biochemistry 1984;23:85–90.

8 Banner DW, Hadvary P: Inhibitor binding to thrombin with x-ray crystallographic studies. Adv Exp Med Biol 1993;340:27–33.

9 Bauer M, Brandstetter H, Turk D, Sturzebekker J, Bode W: Crystallographic determination of thrombin complexes with small synthetic inhibitors as a starting point for the receptor-based design of antithrombotics. Semin Thromb Hemost 1993;19:352–360.

10 Tatsuno J, Komatsu T, Iida S: Pharmacokinetic studies of argatroban (MD-805): Protein binding and blood cell binding. Jap Pharmacol Ther 1986;14(suppl 5):243–249.

11 Berry CN, Girard D, Lochot S, Lecoffre C: Antithrombotic actions of argatroban in rat models of venous, mixed and arterial thrombosis, and its effects on the tail transection bleeding time. Br J Pharmacol 1994;113:1209–1214.

12 Berry CN, Girardot C, Lecoffre C, Lunven C: Effects of the synthetic thrombin inhibitor argatroban on fibrin- or clot-incorporated thrombin: Comparison with heparin and recombinant hirudin. Thromb Haemost 1994;72:381–386.

13 Hantgan RR, Jerome WG, Hursting MJ: No effect of clot age or thrombolysis on argatroban's inhibition of thrombin. Blood 1998;92: 2064–2074.

14 Swan SK, Hursting MJ: The pharmacokinetics and pharmacodynamics of argatroban: Effects of age, gender, and hepatic or renal dysfunction. Pharmacotherapy 2000;20:318–329.

15 Swan SK, St. Peter JV, Lambrecht LJ, Hursting MJ: Comparison of anticoagulant effects and safety of argatroban and heparin in healthy subjects. Pharmacotherapy 2000;20:756–770.

16 Hursting MJ, Joffrion JL, Brooks RL, Swan SK: Effect of renal function on the pharmacokinetics and pharmacodynamics of argatroban (a direct thrombin inhibitor). Blood 1996; 88(suppl 1):167a.

17 Hursting MJ, Becker JC, Joffrion JL, Knappenberger GD, Schwarz RP: Effect of hepatic function on the pharmacokinetics and pharmacodynamics of argatroban. Thromb Haemost 1997(suppl);493–494.

18 Izawa O, Katsuki M, Komatsu T, Iida S: Pharmacokinetics studies of argatroban (MD-805) in human – Concentrations of argatroban and its metabolites in plasma, urine and feces during and after drip intravenous infusion (in Japanese). Jpn Pharmacol Ther 1986;14(suppl 5):251–263.

19 Ahmad S, Ahsan A, George M, Iqbal O, Jeske WP, McKenna R, Lewis BE, Walenga JM, Fareed J: Simultaneous monitoring of argatroban and its major metabolite using an HPLC method: Potential clinical applications. Clin Appl Thromb/Hemost 1999;5:252–258.

20 Walenga JM, Ahmad S, Hoppensteadt D, Iqbal O, Hursting MJ, Lewis BE: Argatroban therapy does not generate antibodies that alter its anticoagulant activity in patients with HIT. Thromb Res 2002;105:401–405.

21 Clark RJ, Mayo G, Fitzgerald GA, Fitzgerald DJ: Combined administration of aspirin and a specific thrombin inhibitor in man. Circulation 1991;83:1510–1518.

22 Tran JQ, DiCicco RA, Sheth SB: Assessment of the potential pharmacokinetic and pharmacodynamic interactions between erythromycin and argatroban. J Clin Pharmacol 1999;39: 513–519.

23 Inglis AL, Sheth SB, Hursting MJ, Tenero DM, Graham AM, DiCicco RA: Investigation of interaction between argatroban and acetaminophen, lidocaine, or digoxin. Am J Health Syst Pharm 2002;59:1258–1266.

24 Walenga JM, Fasanella AR, Iqbal O, Hoppensteadt DA, Ahmad S, Wallis DE, Bakhos M: Coagulation laboratory testing in patients treated with argatroban. Semin Thromb Hemost 1999;25(suppl 1):61–66.

25 Sheth SB, DiCicco RA, Hursting MJ, Montague T, Jorkasky DK: Interpreting the International Normalized Ratio in individuals receiving argatroban and warfarin. Thromb Haemost 2001;85:435–440.

26 Hursting MJ, Zehnder JL, Joffrion JL, Becker JC, Knappenberger GD, Schwarz RP: The International Normalized Ratio during concurrent warfarin and argatroban anticoagulation: Differential contributions of each agent and effects of the choice of thromboplastin used. Clin Chem 1999;45,409–412.

27 Lewis BE, Ferguson JJ, Grassman ED, Fareed J, Walenga JM, Joffrion JL, Wrona L, Johnson SA, Schwarz RP, McKiernan T: Successful coronary interventions performed with argatroban anticoagulation in patients with heparin-induced thrombocytopenia and thrombosis syndrome. J Invas Cardiol 1996;8:410–417.

28 Lewis BE, Wallis DE, Berkowitz SD, Matthai WH, Fareed J, Walenga JM, Bartholomew J for the ARG-911 Study Investigators: Argatroban anticoagulant therapy in patients with heparin-induced thrombocytopenia. Circulation 2001; 103:1838–1843.

29 Lewis BE, Wallis DE, Zehnder JL, Barton JC, for the ARG-911/915/915X investigators: Argatroban reexposure in patients with HIT. Blood 2000;96(pt 1):52a.

30 Lewis BE, Matthai WH Jr, Cohen M, Moses JW, Hursting MJ, Leya F, ARG-216/310/311 Study Investigators: Argatroban anticoagulation during percutaneous coronary intervention in patients with heparin-induced thrombocytopenia. Catheter Cardiovasc Interv 2002; 57:177–184.

31 Itoh T, Nonogi H, Miyazaki S, Itoli A, Daikoko S: Local delivery of argatroban using drug delivery device 'dispatch' in the prevention of restenosis following coronary angioplasty trial (40-CAT): Result of the prospective randomized pilot study. Circulation 1997;96:3635.

32 Kobayashi H, Suzuki S, Sakamoto S, Matsuo T: Argatroban, a direct thrombin inhibitor versus heparin during and after percutaneous transluminal coronary angioplasty (PTCA). Thromb Haemost 1997(suppl);494.
33 Herrman J-P, Suryapranata H, den Heijer P, Gabriël L, Kutryk MJB, Serruys PW: Argatroban during percutaneous transluminal coronary angioplasty: Results of a dose-verification study. J Thromb Thrombolysis 1996;3:367–375.
34 Lewis BE, Rangel Y, Fareed J: The first report of successful carotid stent implant using argatroban anticoagulation in a patient with heparin-induced thrombocytopenia and thrombosis syndrome. Angiology 1998;49:61–67.
35 Lewis BE, Grassman ED, Wrona L, Rangel Y: Novastan anticoagulation during renal stent implant in a patient with HIT. Blood Coagul Fibrinolysis 1997;8:54–58.
36 Kobayashi S, Tazaki Y: Effect of the thrombin inhibitor argatroban in acute cerebral thrombosis. Sem Thromb Hemost 1997;23:531–534.
37 Gold HK, Torres FW, Garabedian HD, Werner W, Jang IK, Khan A, Hagstrom JN, for the study investigators: Evidence for a rebound coagulation phenomenon after cessation of a 4-hour infusion of a specific thrombin inhibitor in patients with unstable angina pectoris. J Am Coll Cardiol 1993;21:1039–1047.
38 Matsuo T, Kario K, Matsuda S, Yamaguchi N, Kakishita E: Effect of thrombin inhibition on patients with peripheral arterial obstructive disease: A multicenter clinical trial of argatroban. J Thromb Thrombolysis 1995;2:131–136.
39 Jang I-K, Brown DF, Giugliano RP, Anderson HV, Losordo D, Nicolau JC, Dutra OP and the MINT investigators: A multicenter, randomized study of argatroban versus heparin as adjunct to TPA in acute myocardial infarction: Myocardial infarction with Novastan and TPA (MINT) trial. J Am Coll Cardiol 1999;33:1879–1885.
40 Vermeer F, Vahanian A, Fels P, Besse P, Muller E, van de Werf F, Fitzgerald D, Darius H, Puel J, Garrigou D, Simoons ML: Argatroban and alteplase in patients with acute myocardial infarction: The ARGAMI study. J Thromb Thrombolysis 2000;10:233–240.
41 Matsuo T, Chikahira Y, Yamada T, Nakao K, Ueshima S, Matsuo O: Effect of synthetic thrombin inhibitor (MD805) as an alternative drug on HIT during hemodialysis. Thromb Res 1988;52:165–171.
42 Koide M, Yamamoto S, Matsuo M, Suzuki S, Arima N, Matsuo T: Anticoagulation for HIT with spontaneous platelet aggregation in a patient requiring haemodialysis. Nephrol Dial Transplant 1995;10:2137–2140.
43 Eichler P, Friesen H-J, Lubenow N, Jaeger B, Greinacher A: Antihirudin antibodies in patients with HIT treated with lepirudin: Incidence, effects on aPTT, and clinical relevance. Blood 2000;96:2373–2378.

Pathophysiology of Haemostasis and Thrombosis

Pathophysiol Haemost Thromb 2002;32(suppl 3):15–22
DOI: 10.1159/000069104

Historical Perspective of the Development of Thrombin Inhibitors

Fritz Markwardt

International Institute of Thrombosis and Vascular Diseases, Erfurt-Frienstedt, Germany

Key Words
Thrombin inhibitors · Heparin · Hirudin · Synthetic inhibitors · Argatroban

Abstract
Progress in molecular biology has stimulated interest in the structure and function of thrombin. It has improved our understanding of its central role in thrombogenesis and has clarified the molecular events of inhibitor binding. This development has resulted in the production of recombinant hirudins and hirudin analogues. It has also allowed the molecular design of synthetic antithrombins, and encouraged the development of these products for clinical use. All pharmacological aspects speak in favor of the use of direct thrombin inhibitors as antithrombotic agents, especially in the potential indications where thrombin plays a crucial pathogenetic role. If their apparent advantages compared with heparin can be definitely demonstrated, the direct thrombin inhibitors may become the drug of choice for certain indications.

Introduction

The clotting enzyme thrombin takes a central position in the blood coagulation system: thrombin catalyzes not only the formation of insoluble fibrin but also activates the clotting factors V, VIII, XIII and protein C, and causes dramatic changes in platelet membrane permeability. Furthermore, it also has direct effects on the vascular endothelium and initiates several nonhemostatic cellular events, such as stimulation of synthesis and release of mediators from the vascular endothelium (fig. 1).

Since the enzymatic activity of thrombin is essential in such bioregulatory events, inhibition of thrombin at blood and vascular sites should be very effective in controlling various pathophysiological states and is vital for the control of thrombogenesis. Therefore, thrombin has become a primary target for the development of antithrombotic agents.

Up to now, pharmacological control of blood coagulation by thrombin inhibition has been possible only with the mammalian glycosaminoglycan heparin. However, its use may cause certain problems. Apart from the necessity of parenteral administration, heparin exerts its inhibitory effect on the clotting enzymes indirectly via a potentiation of the inhibitory function of antithrombin. Therefore, its inhibitory activity depends on the blood level of this plasma protein.

The resulting pharmacological problem has been addressed by the development of thrombin inhibitors different from glycosaminoglycans that block the clotting enzymes directly.

We initially attempted to solve this problem by isolation and pharmacological characterization of inhibitors from blood-sucking animals. These naturally occurring anticoagulants contain specific inhibitors which block either the formation or the effect of thrombin [1, 2].

KARGER
Fax + 41 61 306 12 34
E-Mail karger@karger.ch
www.karger.com

1424–8832/02/0329–0015$18.50/0

Accessible online at:
www.karger.com/pht

Fritz Markwardt
International Institute of Thrombosis and Vascular Diseases
Das Querigfeld 3
D–99192 Erfurt-Frienstedt (Germany)
Tel./Fax +49 36208 70678, E-Mail fmarkwardt@t-online.de

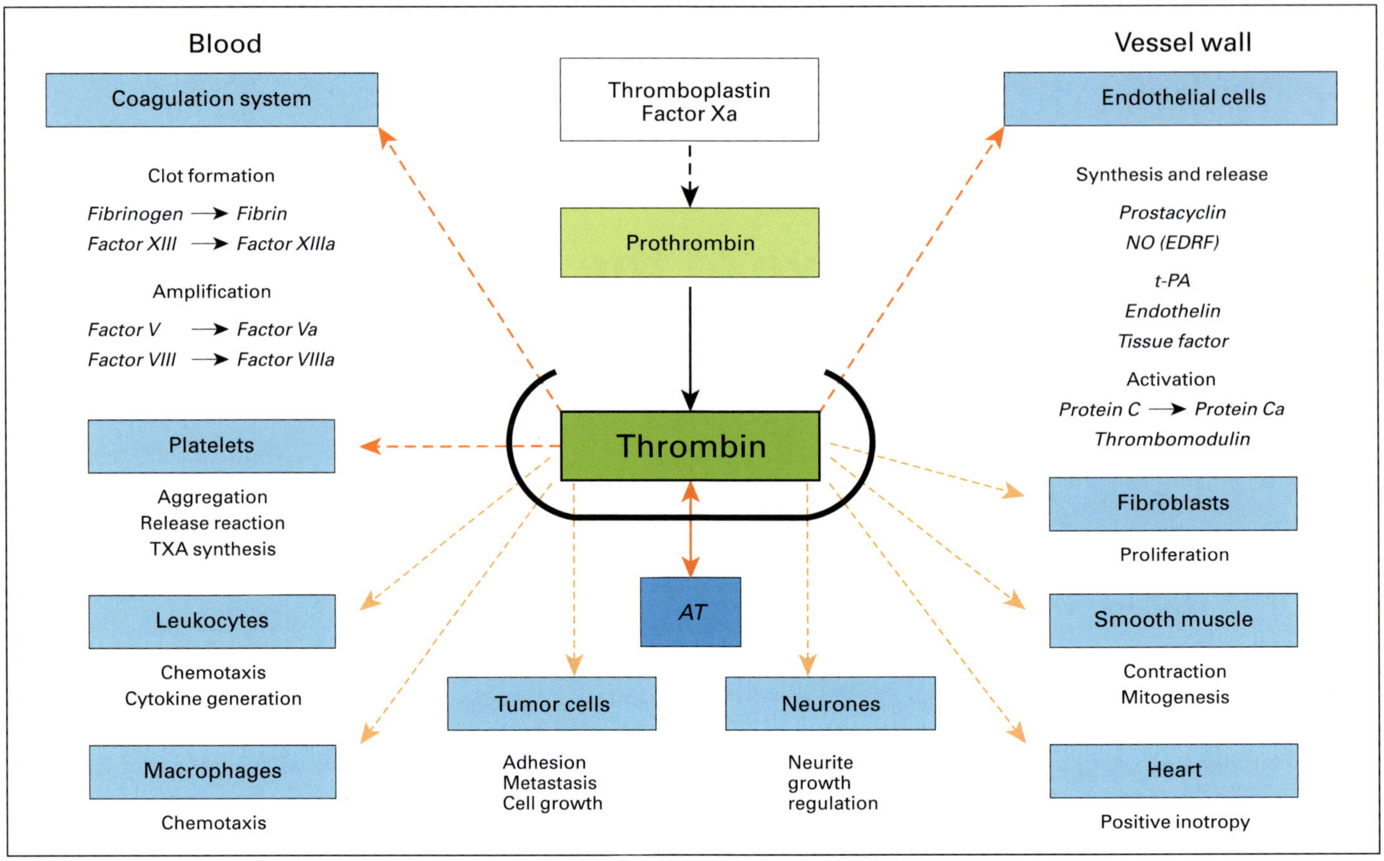

Fig. 1. Inhibition of hemostatic and nonhemostatic effects of thrombin by direct thrombin inhibitors (----).

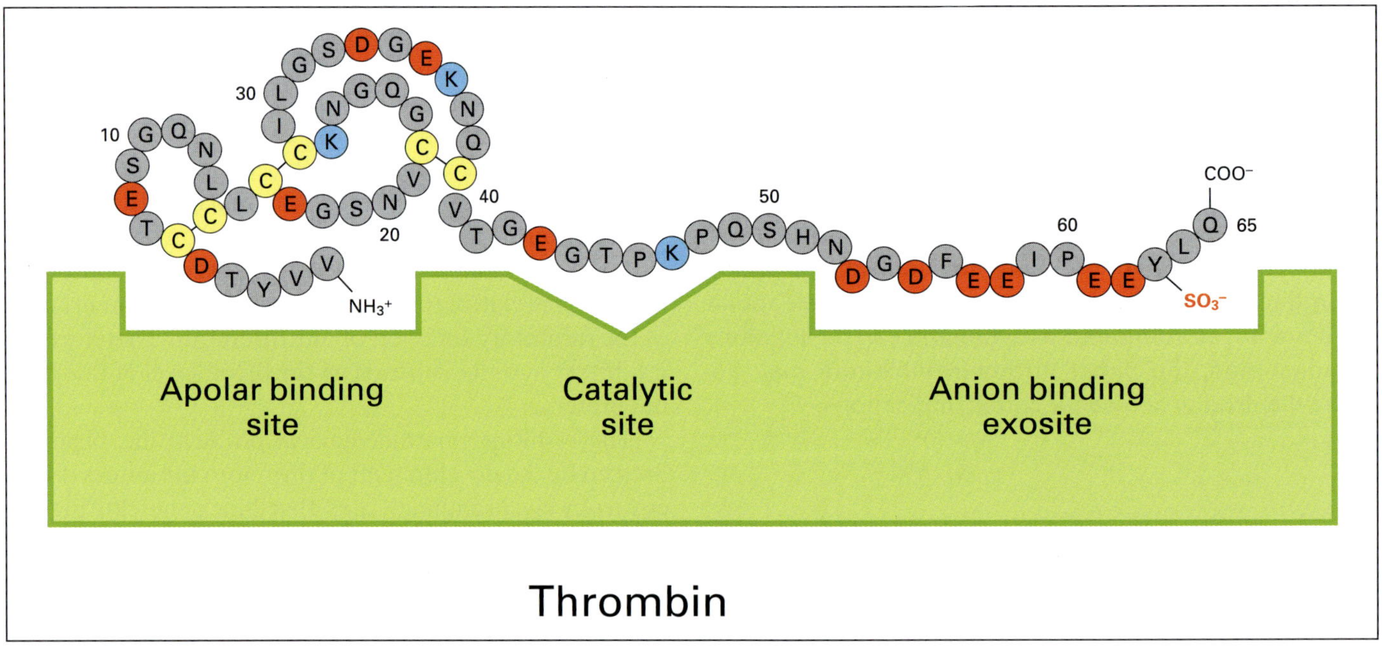

Fig. 2. Primary structure of native hirudin (variant 1, HV1) (amino acids are shown with the single letter code) and schematic representation of the hirudin-thrombin reaction.

Table 1. Synopsis of thrombin inhibitors

Characteristics	Chemical nature (type)
Hirudin and other specific inhibitors from hematophages	Natural and recombinant miniproteins (desirudin, lepirudin)
Chimeric inhibitors, analogues to hirudin	Synthetic bifunctional oligopeptides (hirulog)
Substrate-derived competitive inhibitors	Peptid arginals and derivatives (efegatran, inogatran, melagatran)
Mechanism-based inhibitors, heterocyclic compounds	Peptidomimetics (argatroban, napsagatran)

Isolation and sequencing of the inhibitors allowed molecular cloning of the corresponding cDNA, and synthetic genes coding for the inhibitors could be expressed in *Escherichia coli* or yeast. Therefore, most of the inhibitors have undergone genetic engineering and are now available as recombinant peptides in adequate amounts for experimental and clinical pharmacological studies [3, 4].

The specific thrombin inhibitor produced by the medicinal leech *(Hirudo medicinalis)*, named hirudin, was isolated and characterized as a specific high-affinity thrombin inhibitor in the late 1950s. It is a potent specific inhibitor of thrombin and has served as a standard for designing new inhibitors [5–7].

Recombinant Hirudin

As a consequence of biotechnological production methods, recombinant products allowed the introduction of the most potent natural inhibitor of thrombin as a clinical anticoagulant. Several structural variants of hirudin were produced by recombinant DNA technologies including point mutations and N-terminal modifications (desirudin, lepirudin). This process led to new insights into structure-activity relationships of this unique and promising thrombin inhibitor [8–13].

Hirudin has an unusual asymmetry of structural elements. A compact, hydrophobic core region in the amino-terminal half of the molecule contains alternating polar and nonpolar segments and all three disulfide bonds. The carboxy-terminal region is more extended and extremely hydrophilic.

The crystallographic structure of the hirudin-thrombin complex shows the structural regions of the enzyme and the inhibitor involved in the thrombin-hirudin interaction. It confirms the high affinity of hirudin for thrombin and the specificity of the tight and essentially irreversible binding of hirudin to thrombin (fig. 2).

Synthetic Thrombin Inhibitors

The limitations of antithrombotic therapy with heparin and analogues and the lessons learned from the clinical use of hirudin have a great impact on the development of synthetic low molecular antithrombin agents as anticoagulant and potential antithrombotic drugs [14].

Through the mid 1970s, several laboratories synthesized large numbers of thrombin inhibitors. The major milestone in this field was the breakthrough achieved in determining the crystal structure of thrombin. The availability of this structure together with the elucidation of structural features of hirudin provides a rational basis for the design and synthesis of peptide and nonpeptide thrombin inhibitors [15–18].

Only a few compounds among the numerous synthetic thrombin inhibitors described have proved to be suitable as anticoagulants. Table 1 presents a synopsis of these inhibitors.

Oligopeptides

A series of synthetic bifunctional oligopeptides has been modeled according to the natural peptide. Coupling of peptides that mimic the carboxy terminal of hirudin to peptides that are specific for inhibition of the catalytic site of thrombin (*D*-Phe-Pro-Arg) has led to the development of a series of chimeric molecules termed hirulogs, in which the exosite recognition sequence of the hirudin C-terminus is linked by glycyl residues to a potent ligand directed at the catalytic site (hirulog) [19].

Peptide Arginals and Derivatives

The development of synthetic thrombin inhibitors is a new example of designing protease inhibitors through the mimicry of substrates. Imitating the amino sequence around the thrombin-scissible bond in fibrinogen, inhibi-

Fig. 3. Schematic representation of the reaction of thrombin with direct inhibitors. The catalytic site (C), the anion-binding exosite (B), and the apolar region (A) are the three functional domains of the thrombin molecule that interact with direct thrombin inhibitors. The active site C contains the catalytic triad (serine/histidine/aspartic acid). It forms a specific pocket that binds the basic arginine and lysine residues of site-directed thrombin inhibitors. The anion-binding exosite (B) (also known as substrate recognition site) is located in a region of the thrombin molecule distant from the catalytic site. It is comprised of multiple basic amino acids that permit it to form ionic bonds with the carboxyl terminus of some natural thrombin inhibitors. The apolar region (A) bonds via hydrophobic interactions with the aminoterminals of natural thrombin inhibitors as well as with hydrophilic groups of synthetic inhibitors.

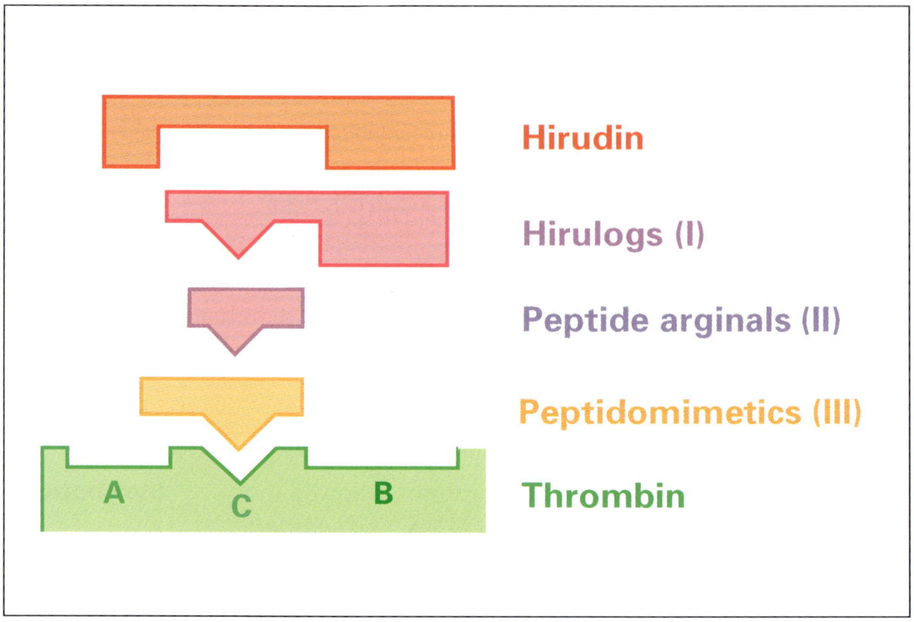

tors were produced that enter into a covalent or non-covalent bond with the active site of the enzyme.

The most useful skeleton in designing active-site-directed thrombin inhibitors was the sequence Phe-Pro-Arg-H, especially if phenylalanine is in the *D*-configuration [20]. A series of derivatives of the prototype tripeptide aldehyde has been developed as reversible thrombin inhibitors (*D*-MePhe-Pro-Arg-H, efegatran; HOOCCH$_2$-*D*-Cha-Pip-Nag, inogatran; HOOCCH$_2$-D-Chg-Aze-Pab, melagatran).

Furthermore, the highly selective affinity label for thrombin, *D*-Phe-Pro-Arg-CH$_2$Cl (PPACK), is effective as a covalently binding irreversible thrombin inhibitor. By substitution of the sequence with other reactive groups (for example boronic acid, Ac-*D*-Phe-Pro-boroArg) additional thrombin inhibitors were obtained.

Peptidomimetics

Modification of substrates is a common principle for designing inhibitors. One of the building blocks used to develop synthetic inhibitors is arginine with optimal C- and/or N-terminal modifications.

Starting from the synthetic thrombin substrate Nα-tosyl-*L*-arginine methyl ester (TAME), Okamoto and his group have designed competitive inhibitors of considerable potency and selectivity by variation of the carbonyl and Nα-substituents [21, 22]. Tmq-Arg-*D*-Pip(4-Me)-OH, argatroban, one of the representatives of the peptidomimetic thrombin inhibitors, has reached the stage of advanced clinical trials and is now available for treatment.

Our group focused on derivatives of benzamidine, which are isosteric to arginine amides and are able to mimic the protonated basic guanidinoalkyl side chain of arginine. Thus we found pseudopeptides possessing structures similar to peptidyl inhibitors (βNas-Gly-*D*-(4-Am)Phe-Ppd, NAPAP) [23, 24].

An alternative building block used to develop small inhibitors for the catalytic site of thrombin is amidinopiperidine. Modifications of this molecule yielded competitive inhibitors for thrombin (βNas-Asp(O-NPG)Phe-Ppd, napsagatran).

In order to evaluate the potential usefulness of the direct thrombin inhibitor for therapeutic purposes, a special program of in vitro and in vivo investigations was established [25–28].

Anticoagulant Action

The anticoagulant action of the inhibitors is one of the first biological effects to be tested after biochemical studies on their enzyme inhibitory activity. A scheme of their mode of action is shown in figure 3.

By instantaneous inhibition of the small amount of thrombin generated after activation of the clotting system, the positive feedback on prothrombin activation – that would normally lead to accelerated generation of thrombin – is prevented and thrombin generation is delayed. Thus, depending on the inhibitor concentration in blood, coagulation is retarded or completely inhibited.

Moreover, thrombin inhibitors not only prevent thrombin-catalyzed hemostatic reactions including the thrombin-induced platelet aggregation and release reaction, but also the synthesis and release of some mediators from the vascular endothelium and the binding of thrombin to endothelial thrombomodulin. In addition, they will interfere with all the humoral effects of thrombin, such as proliferation of fibroblasts and contraction and mitogenesis of smooth muscle cells. In particular, the vasoconstrictor action of thrombin in deendothelialized vessels may be inhibited. Thus, the specific thrombin inhibitors may interfere with essential vascular mechanisms of thrombosis (fig. 1).

Antithrombotic Effects

The efficacy of thrombin inhibitors in preventing venous and arterial thrombosis was demonstrated in various animal models in which the pathological mechanism largely corresponded to those of thromboembolic disorders in man. The anti-thrombotic effect was confirmed by prevention of thrombi induced in the venous stasis model. It was demonstrated in arterial thrombosis induced by vessel wall lesions. Reocclusion after experimental thrombolysis and angioplasty was also inhibited. The prevention of microthrombosis was repeatedly demonstrated in disseminated intravascular coagulation. The efficiency in preventing clot formation on artificial surfaces was quantified by experiments in which materials of varying thrombogenicity were placed in an extracorporeal circuit [26, 27].

Even if the clinical relevance of thrombosis models in experimental animals remains debatable, the antithrombotic effectiveness of the direct thrombin inhibitors has been clearly demonstrated. In general, their outstanding efficacy became obvious when thrombin was initially formed by diffuse intrinsic or extrinsic activation of the coagulation pathway. Stasis-induced venous thrombosis and disseminated microthrombosis were most sensitive. Comparatively higher doses were required in arterial thrombosis and extracorporeal shunt thrombosis, in which platelets play a role. These differences may be explained by the finding that the inhibition of the thrombin-platelet reaction requires higher inhibitor concentrations than that of the thrombin-fibrinogen reaction.

Clinico-pharmacologic studies corroborated the specific pharmacological properties of the site-directed antithrombin agents such as hirudin, oligopeptides, synthetic tripeptides derivatives and peptidomimetics found in animal experiments. The new thrombin inhibitors are currently undergoing various phases of clinical trials. Moreover, for a broader clinical application of thrombin inhibitors as antithrombotics the following issues warrant consideration.

Pharmacokinetics

Thrombin inhibitors do not find a preformed, permanent systemic target in the organism. Instead, their specific binding site is present only when the target enzyme is generated. Therefore, the effect of thrombin inhibitors in vivo depends on their pharmacokinetic behavior, especially the time course of their blood levels.

The pharmacokinetic behavior of hirudin can best be described by an open two-compartment model with first-order kinetics. Following an intravenous bolus injection, hirudin is distributed into the extracellular space and predominantly excreted in the urine with a half-life of 60 min. After subcutaneous administration, peak plasma levels were reached after 1–2 h and bioavailability was calculated as 70–80%. There is some absorption of hirudin after intratracheal instillation. Rectal or intraduodenal and percutaneous administration did not lead to detectable plasma levels [29].

The percentage of the dose that was renally excreted in unmodified form differed in various species. The activity lasted longer in anephric animals, suggesting that the kidney is a major route of elimination. Accordingly, hirudin elimination from blood can be retarded by coupling to biomacromolecules, such as dextran or polyethylene glycol [30–32].

The short biological half-life of synthetic thrombin inhibitors, ranging from 10 to 60 min, represents a limitation for their broader clinical application. Poor mucous membrane permeation and/or extensive hepatic first pass effect is probably the reason for the lack of activity after oral administration of these inhibitors, which have to be classified as parenteral thrombin inhibitors.

There is a need for an orally applicable formulation of a synthetic thrombin inhibitor that achieves a prolonged inhibition of thrombin. The aim to find substances which are active when administered orally is a goal to be achieved for this new class of drugs and will become an active field of pharmacological research in the future.

Hemostasis

One of the drawbacks of anticoagulants is that hemostasis is impaired and thus entails a risk of bleeding. But therapeutic doses of thrombin inhibitors were tolerated without adverse effects, in particular bleeding tendencies,

Table 2. Comparison of pharmacological properties of antithrombin agents

Heparin	Hirudin	Synthetic inhibitors
Family of sulfated glycosaminoglycans	Single-chain polypeptide	Peptides or peptidomimetics
Isolation and purification procedures	Expensive production genetic engineering	Less expensive chemical preparation
Multiple sites of action, potentiate inactivation of clotting enzymes by plasma inhibitors	Selective, tight binding inhibitor acts by inhibiting thrombin-mediated coagulation	Specific, direct inhibitors acting by competitive inhibition of the clotting enzyme
Requires endogenous cofactors (ATIII)	Does not require cofactors	Does not require cofactors
Interaction with endothelium and plasma proteins	Not susceptible to blood constituents	Limited effect on blood constituents
Direct or immune-mediated platelet activation	No direct effects on platelets	No direct effects on platelets
No activity against clot-bound thrombin	Limited activity against clot-bound thrombin	Inhibits clot-bound thrombin
Neutralized by antiheparins, metabolized in liver degradation	Mainly excreted in unchanged form in the urine	Hepatic uptake, biliary excretion metabolic
Further prospects Low molecular weight heparin fractions and analogues	Polyethylene-glycol-coupled recombinant analogues	Derivatives with oral availability

unless administered at doses considerably higher than required for antithrombotic efficiency [33].

Nevertheless, it is desirable to have antidotes available against any unexpected bleeding, i.e. an antagonist. In contrast to heparin, which could be neutralized by protamine, no specific antidote against thrombin inhibitors can be recommended at present. However, as revealed by our experimental studies, several possibilities exist. Prohemostatic agents, such as prothrombin complex concentrates, could antagonize the anticoagulant effects. They furnish thrombin, which forms an inactive complex with the thrombin inhibitor. Furthermore, chemical and genetically modified thrombin and meizothrombin, that are not prothrombotic but still bind to thrombin inhibitors, neutralize the antithrombotic agents. However, these antidotes still need careful preclinical and clinical evaluation.

Special Indications

A comparison of the pharmacological characteristics of the antithrombin agents illustrates the progress and problems in the development of direct thrombin inhibitors (table 2).

Short peptides or peptide analogues have the advantage of being less expensive to prepare. They have the potential to be orally active. In contrast to hirudin and its analogues, synthetic inhibitors have lower specificity, possess side chains or reactive groups, which can react with various plasma components producing side effects and leading to relatively rapid loss of activity in blood, besides their hepatic metabolism.

Direct thrombin inhibitors, either the naturally occurring or recombinant and the synthetic ones, are novel antithrombotic agents in a field where heparin has been the only available drug so far [34].

Compared with heparin, thrombin inhibitors possess a number of advantages since they do not require the presence of endogenous cofactors like antithrombin III. Hence patients with deficiencies in this protein, as is the case in disseminated intravascular coagulation, can be treated with direct thrombin inhibitors.

Furthermore, thrombin inhibitors are not bound or inactivated by platelet factors or other proteins acting as antiheparin substances. They have no influence on platelet function and no direct or immune-mediated platelet-activating properties. Therefore, they should be advantageous under conditions in which platelet defects or heparin-induced thrombocytopenia may present a risk.

For the effect in thrombosis it is of interest that the inhibitors – in contrast to the heparin-antithrombin complex – are able to block thrombin bound to the fibrin network, whereby the growth of preexistent thrombi can be prevented and thrombin which might be released during endogenous thrombolysis was inhibited. Therefore, thrombin inhibitors may be suited as a postoperative prophylactic agent.

The central role of thrombosis in the pathogenesis of acute myocardial infarction, unstable angina, and complications after angioplasty (especially reocclusion) has led to intense interest in developing antithrombin agents for the management of coronary ischemic syndromes. Thrombin inhibitors also were used in the management of extracorporeal circulation and hemodialysis.

The pathophysiological role of thrombin, extending beyond coagulation and platelet activation, suggests that thrombin inhibitors could equally be used as therapeutic tools in areas other than blood coagulation. Indeed, effects of thrombin on other cell types and function, ranging from mitogenesis and contraction of smooth muscle cells to adhesion and metastasis of tumor cells, were inhibited. Although the functions of thrombin in such processes have not been fully characterized, areas covered by antithrombin drugs could include acute inflammatory response, tissue repair, and modulation of cellular viability.

Conclusion

The production of naturally occurring and synthetic thrombin inhibitors has encouraged the development of these products as antithrombotic agents. All pharmacological aspects speak in favor of the clinical use of direct antithrombins especially in potential indications where thrombin plays a crucial role in the pathogenesis.

Demonstration of their ultimate clinical utility and advantages, however, represents a substantial challenge and has led to fundamental questions:

- Will thrombin inhibitors be substitutes, supplements, or successors to heparin?
- Which clotting assay can best predict the antithrombotic effect?
- What is the therapeutic window in different clinical settings?

Moreover, considering the multiple functions of thrombin, it remains to be clarified whether thrombin inhibitors might also have other indications than prevention of acute thrombotic events.

References

1 Markwardt F: Blutgerinnungshemmende Wirkstoffe aus blutsaugenden Tieren. Jena, Gustav Fischer, 1963.

2 Markwardt F, Landmann H: Blutgerinnungshemmende Proteine, Peptide und Aminosäurederivate; in Markwardt F (ed): Handbuch der experimentellen Pharmakologie. Berlin, Springer, 1971, vol 27: Anticoagulantien, pp 76–142.

3 Markwardt F: Coagulation inhibitors of bloodsucking animals – A new line of developing antithrombotic drugs. Pharmazie 1993;49: 313–316.

4 Markwardt F: Antithrombotic agents from hematophagous animals. Clin Appl Thromb Hemost 1996;2:75–82.

5 Markwardt F: Isolierung und chemische Charakterisierung des Hirudins. Hoppe Seylers Z Physiol Chem 1957;308:147–156.

6 Markwardt F, Walsmann: Reindarstellung und Analyse des Thrombin-Inhibitors Hirudin. Hoppe Seylers Z Physiol Chem 1967;348: 1381–1386.

7 Markwardt F: Hirudin as an inhibitor of thrombin; in Colowick SP, Kaplan NO (eds): Methods in Enzymology. New York, Academic Press, 1970, vol 19: Proteolytic Enzymes, pp 924–932.

8 Markwardt F, Fink E, Kaiser B, Klöcking HP, Nowack G, Richter M, Stürzebecher J: Pharmacological survey of recombinant hirudin. Pharmazie 1988;43:202–207.

9 Markwardt F: Development of hirudin as an antithrombotic agent. Semin Thromb Hemost 1989;15:269–282.

10 Markwardt F: Hirudin and derivatives as anticoagulant agents. Thromb Haemost 1991;66: 141–152.

11 Markwardt F: Past, present and future of hirudin. Haemostasis 1991;21(suppl1):11–26.

12 Markwardt F: Le génie génétique conduit au retour de l'hirudine comme anticoagulant. Sang Thrombos Vaisseaux 1991;3:519–522.

13 Markwardt F: The development of hirudin as an antithrombotic drug. Thromb Res 1994;74: 1–23.

14 Markwardt F: Synthetic, low molecular thrombin inhibitors. A new concept of anticoagulants? Haemostasis 1974;3:185–202.

15 Markwardt F: Pharmacological control of hyperproteolytic states in blood by synthetic inhibitors of serine proteinases. Haemostasis1978:7:177–182.

16 Markwardt F: Pharmacological control of blood coagulation by synthetic low-molecular-weight inhibitors of clotting enzymes. A new concept of anticoagulants. Trends Pharmacol Sci 1980;1:153–157.

17 Hauptmann J, Markwardt F: Pharmacological aspects of the development of selective synthetic thrombin inhibitors as anticoagulants. Semin Thromb Hemost 1992;18:200–217.

18 Hauptmann J, Stürzebecher J: Synthetic inhibitors of thrombin and factor Xa: From bench to bedside. Thromb Res 1999;93:203–241.

19 Marganore JM, Bourdon P, Jablonski J, Ramachandran KJ: Design and characterization of hirulogs, A novel class of bivalent peptide inhibitors of thrombin. Biochemistry 1998;29: 7095–7101.

20 Bajusz S, Szeli E, Bagdy D, Barabas E, Horvath G, Diosszegi M, Szabo G, Juhasz A, Tomori E, Szilagy G: Highly active and selective anticoagulants: *D*-Phe-Pro-Arg-H, a free tripeptide aldehyde prone to spontaneous inactivation, and its stable M-methyl derivative, *D*-MePhe-Pro-ArgH. J Med Chem 1990;33:1729–1735.

21 Okamoto S, Kinjo K, Hijikata A: Thrombin inhibitors. 1. Ester derivatives of Nα-(arylsulfonyl)-arginine. J Med Chem 1980;23:827–830.

22 Matsuo T, Kario K, Kodama K, Okamoto S: Clinical applications of the synthetic thrombin inhibitor, argatroban (MD 805). Semin Thromb Hemost 1992;18:216–218.

23 Stürzebecher J, Markwardt F, Voigt B, Wagner G, Walsmann P: Cyclic amides of Nα-arylsulfonylaminoacylated 4- amidinophenylalanin – tight binding inhibitors of thrombin. Thromb Res 1983;29:635–642.

24 Kaiser B. Hauptmann J, Weiss A, Markwardt F: Pharmacological characterisation of a new highly effective synthetic thrombin inhibitor. Biomed Biochim Acta 1985;44:1201–1210.
25 Markwardt F, Hauptmann J, Nowak G, Klessen C, Walsmann P: Pharmacological studies on the antithrombotic action of hirudin in experimental animals. Thromb Haemost 1982; 47:226–229.
26 Markwardt F, Kaiser B, Nowak G: Studies on antithrombotic effects of recombinant hirudin. Thromb Res 1989;54:377–388.
27 Markwardt F, Klöcking HP: Antithrombotic effect of synthetic thrombin inhibitors. Thromb Res 1972;1:243–252.
28 Markwardt, F: Pharmacology of selective thrombin inhibitors. Nouv Rev Fr Hématol 1988;30:161–165.
29 Markwardt F, Nowak G, Stürzebecher J: Clinical pharmacology of recombinant hirudin. Haemostasis 1991;21:133–136.
30 Richter M, Walsmann P, Markwardt F: Plasma level of dextran-r-hirudin. Pharmazie 1989;44: 73.
31 Markwardt F, Richter M, Walsmann P, Riesener G. Paintz M: Preparation of dextran-bound recombinant hirudin and its pharmacokinetic behavior. Biomed Biochim Acta 1990; 49:1103–1126.
32 Rübsamen K, Hornberger W, Schweden J, Kurfürst M: Pharmacological characterization of a long acting polyethylen glycol-coupled recombinant hirudin. Thromb Haemost 1991; 65:1291.
33 Kaiser B, Markwardt F: Antithrombotic and haemorrhagic effects of synthetic and naturally occurring thrombin inhibitors. Thromb Res 1986;43:613–620.
34 Markwardt F: Development of direct thrombin inhibitors in comparison to glycosaminoglycans. Semin Thromb Hemost 2001;27:523–530.

Pathophysiology of Haemostasis and Thrombosis

Pathophysiol Haemost Thromb 2002;32(suppl 3):23–28
DOI: 10.1159/000069105

Development of Argatroban as an Anticoagulant and Antithrombin Agent in Japan

Hidenobu Ikoma

Development Coordination Department, Pharmaceuticals Development Unit, Research and Development Division,
Mitsubishi Pharma Corporation, Tokyo, Japan

Key Words
Argatroban · Direct thrombin inhibitor · Cerebral thrombosis · Chronic arterial occlusion · Hemodialysis in AT deficiency

Abstract
Argatroban is a synthetic direct thrombin inhibitor which has been used in Japan for three indications, namely, chronic arterial occlusion, acute cerebral thrombosis and hemodialysis in AT-deficient patients or in patients with decreased AT. In patients with chronic arterial occlusion, argatroban increased the skin temperature, reduced the size of skin ulcers, and decreased the thrombin-antithrombin complex. In patients with acute cerebral thrombosis, neuronal symptoms improved significantly compared with the placebo group, wherein activated partial thromboplastin time (aPTT) was prolonged by about 1.5-fold and fibrinopeptide A was reduced. In some patients in whom hemodialysis is difficult due to the generation of blood clots in the dialyzer, hemodialysis is now possible with the replacement of heparin by argatroban.

Introduction

Argatroban has been approved for three indications in Japan. In 1990, argatroban was approved as an anticoagulant for chronic arterial occlusion. In 1996, approval was granted for the additional indications of acute cerebral thrombosis and for the treatment of hemodialysis patients who are antithrombin (AT) deficient or with decreased AT.

Outside Japan, argatroban was approved by the FDA as an anticoagulant for the prophylaxis or treatment of thrombosis in patients with heparin-induced thrombocytopenia (HIT). Argatroban has been launched in Korea for chronic arterial occlusion and acute cerebral thrombosis. Argatroban has also been approved for use in Canada.

This paper provides an overview of the history of the development of argatroban in Japan and the effect of the drug on coagulation tests in the three indications of acute cerebral thrombosis, chronic arterial occlusion, and hemodialysis in AT-deficient patients or patients with decreased AT. Details of the approved indications in Japan are as follows:

(1) acute cerebral thrombosis: improvement of neurological symptoms (paralysis) accompanying the disease and improvement of activities of daily living (ADL)

KARGER
Fax + 41 61 306 12 34
E-Mail karger@karger.ch
www.karger.com

1424–8832/02/0329–0023$18.50/0

Accessible online at:
www.karger.com/pht

Hidenobu Ikoma, Clinical Development Department 1
Research and Development Division, Mitsubishi-Tokyo Pharmaceutical, Inc.
2-2-6 Nihonbashi-Honcho, Chuo-ku, Tokyo 103-8405 (Japan)
Tel. +81 3 3242 4391, Fax +81 3 3241 4807
E-Mail Ikoma.Hidenobu@mh.m-pharma.co.jp

(which involves the ability to walk, stand up, maintain a sitting position, and take meals); (a) acute cerebral thrombosis (excluding lacunes) within 48 h after onset;

(2) improvement in limb ulcers, rest pain, and a sensation of cold accompanying chronic arterial occlusion (Buerger's disease, arteriosclerosis obliterans);

(3) prevention of clotting in the perfused blood during extracorporeal circulation in the following patients: (a) congenital AT-deficient patients or patients with decreased AT; (b) patients with reduced AT levels (patients where AT is <70% normal values or where heparin treatment produces no improvement in clotting (residual blood) during extracorporeal circulation).

History of Development in Japan

Thrombosis is thought to occur as a result of an imbalance in the blood coagulation-fibrinolytic system that produces a tendency to clot. Thrombin plays a very important role in the blood coagulation system. Thrombin not only converts fibrinogen to fibrin, but it also initiates platelet aggregation, and blood vessel constriction.

Research was started in this area on the basis that substances that suppress the thrombus-forming activity of thrombin may be promising in drug therapy for thrombosis. In 1972, research by Mitsubishi Chemical Industries and Okamoto et al. [1] showed that thrombin promotes the conversion of fibrinogen to fibrin by cutting the Arg-Gly bond in fibrinogen. Starting with a thrombin inhibitor, tosyl arginyl methyl ester, research began on the development of a potent and selective antithrombin drug through the substitution of the arginine carbonyl group and amino group.

The results of this research showed that argatroban inhibited thrombin at extremely low concentrations and that the drug had an extremely weak inhibitory effect on trypsin (also a serine protease), factor Xa, plasmin, and kallikrein [2]. These results confirmed the concept that argatroban selectively inhibits thrombin.

Pharmacological Effects of Argatroban

Argatroban binds reversibly to thrombin and its effects are short-lived [3]. The therapeutic effects of argatroban can be easily monitored by anticoagulation tests (such as aPTT or prothrombin time (PT)), so anticoagulation therapy with argatroban is easy to control. Argatroban is highly selective for thrombin. The molecular weight is low (527 Da). Thus, argatroban can bind not only to circulating thrombin but also to clot-bound thrombin, unlike heparins that bind solely to circulating thrombin [4]. Argatroban does not require the cofactor AT for antithrombotic activity, in contrast to heparins and heparinoids [5]. Thus, argatroban can exert its effect even in AT-deficient patients and in patients with decreased AT [6]. Finally, unlike heparins, argatroban does not generate antibodies and, unlike heparinoids and low molecular weight heparins, argatroban does not cross-react with heparin antibodies [7].

In addition to the pharmacological profile shown above, argatroban demonstrates several other important actions. In vitro studies have shown that argatroban inhibits thrombin-mediated endothelin-1 release from the endothelium [8], inhibits thrombin-mediated vascular constriction [9], and increases the effect of thrombolytic agents such as tissue plasminogen activator (t-PA) [10]. Moreover, in terms of its anticoagulant action, argatroban differs from heparin in vitro in that it produces no excessive prolongation of the aPTT in a wide range of concentrations, while heparin produces marked prolongation of aPTT at a narrow range of concentrations [11] (fig. 1). Intravenous administration of heparin (1,000 IU) or argatroban (6 mg) for 2 h produces an exponential prolongation of aPTT during the infusion with heparin, but a plateau at approximately 30 min after commencing the argatroban infusion [12] (fig. 1). Thus, there is considerable control of coagulation during the argatroban infusion.

Argatroban and Chronic Arterial Occlusion

In chronic arterial occlusion, for which argatroban is indicated, the thrombus forms in the blood vessel lumen and repeatedly exacerbates or rekindles ischemic symptoms. In addition to ischemic symptoms such as cold, cyanosis, rest pain, and intermittent claudication, the disease can worsen limb ulcers and many cases require amputation.

A pivotal study [13] using a double dummy method compared with argatroban (twice daily doses of 10 mg given by intravenous infusion over 3 h, for 4 weeks) with the antiplatelet agent ticlopidine (500 mg/day by oral administration for 6 weeks). Results in the argatroban group were equivalent to those in the panaldine group, in terms of degree of ulcer reduction and improvement in rest pain and cold. Argatroban, however, has a rapid onset of action and is effective in cases not improved by treatment with

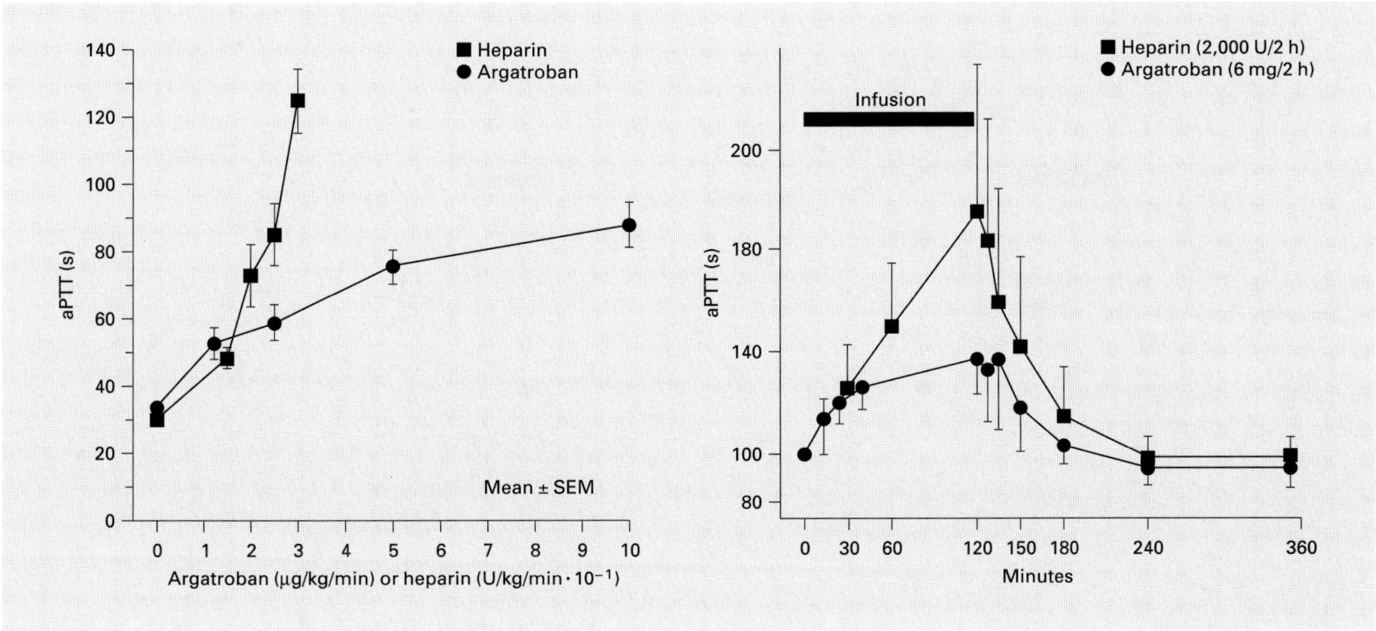

Fig. 1. Effects of continuous infusions (2 h) of heparin or argatroban on aPTT in healthy subjects. From Fukutake et al. [12] (with slight modification).

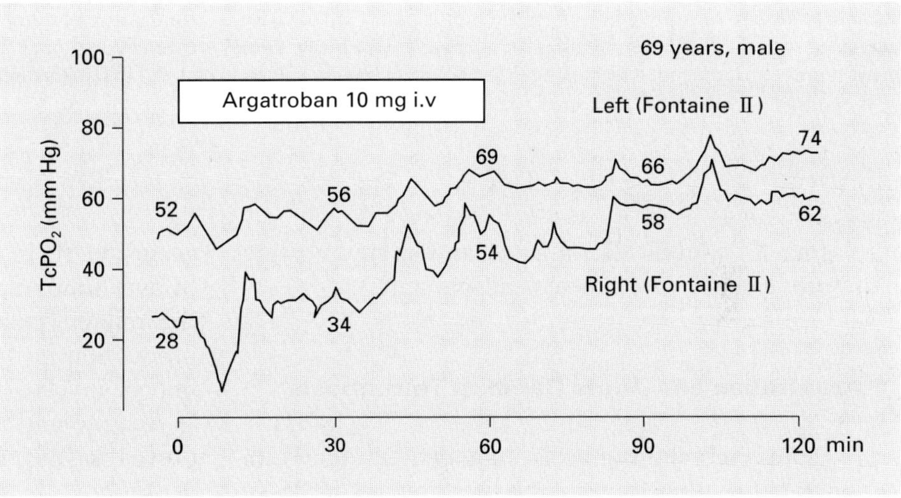

Fig. 2. Transcutaneous tissue oxygen partial pressure ($TcPO_2$) of skin surface of a patient with chronic arterial occlusion. From Itoh et al. [14] (with slight modification).

antiplatelet, vasodilators, or other agents. Moreover, when 10 mg argatroban was administered intravenously for 1 h, the drug increased the transcutaneous tissue oxygen partial pressure ($TcPO_2$) at the skin surface of the diseased leg more than the healthy leg (fig. 2). The results also confirmed increased skin temperature and $TcPO_2$ in the diseased leg in severe cases, compared with mild cases [14]. This effect persisted regardless of the low blood concentration of argatroban after infusion. However, heparin was shown to have almost no influence on the peripheral circulation.

In patients with chronic arterial occlusion, argatroban produced a decrease in thrombin-antithrombin complex (TAT), which is an indicator of thrombin formation [15]. TAT levels after argatroban therapy were decreased in patients with chronic arterial occlusion. The decrease

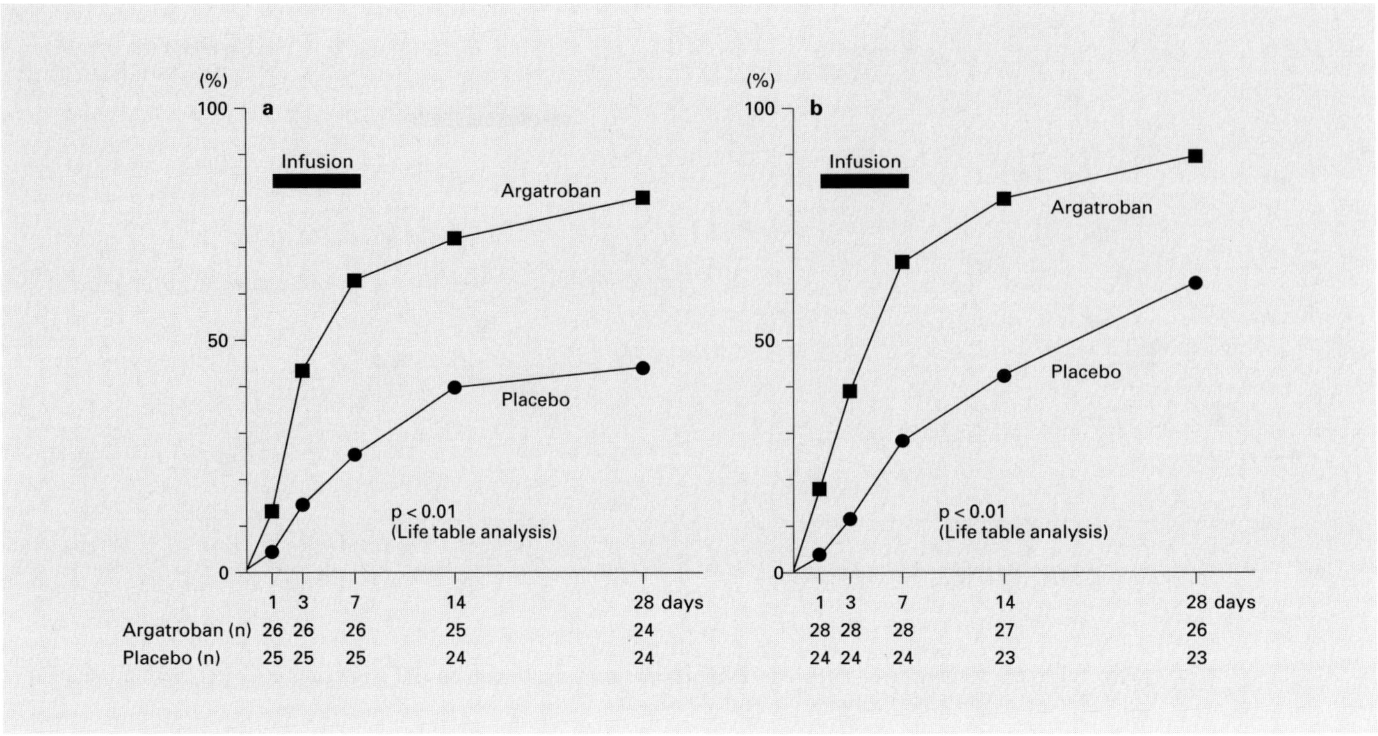

Fig. 3. Percentage of patients who showed more than one rank improvement in the symptom scale during treatment **a** Paralyzed leg scale. The degree of muscle power on the motor paralyzed side was classified into the following 4 grades: 0: normal; 1: can move ankle against gravity; 2: extended leg raising or knee flexion possible; 3: can move only on floor, or unable to move at all. **b** ADL scale. ADL was classified into the following 4 grades: 0: normal (no symptoms); 1: mild (can care almost by oneself, but slow in action); 2: moderate (needs assistance); 3: severe (cannot perform at all). From Kobayashi et al. [18] (with slight modification).

in plasma TAT levels after argatroban therapy indicates an improvement in the hypercoagulable state.

Argatroban and Acute Cerebral Thrombosis

In acute cerebral thrombosis, another argatroban indication, the thrombus forms at the site of a vascular lesion producing occlusive symptoms, and new symptoms occur over time after the initial onset of symptoms, accompanying enlargement of the ischemic area. Symptoms usually stabilize after several hours or days [16].

This concept is supported by reports of the following research into coagulation after symptom onset. A study in patients after the onset of cerebral thrombosis has shown that fibrinopeptide A (FPA), an indicator of thrombin activity, increases until 7 days after symptom onset, with a peak at 3 days after onset [17]. In cerebral infarction patients and cerebral thrombosis models after thrombotic occlusion, there is secondary formation of minute thrombi over time, mainly involving fibrin [16]. This impairs the microcirculation, resulting in continued thrombin production in the acute phase after symptom onset and may be involved in the hypercoagulable state.

Symptomatic improvement may be due to argatroban preventing the progression of the infarct into the ischemic penumbra.

In acute cerebral thrombosis, a pivotal study on argatroban compared the drug with placebo in a double-blind trial [18]. Patients were given continuous drip infusions for the first 2 days (60 mg/day) followed by twice-daily infusions (10 mg × 2) for 3 h each on days 3–7. In comparison with placebo, a significant difference was seen in the argatroban group in terms of improvement of neurological symptoms (upper and lower paralysis-paralysed leg scale) and ADL (ability to walk, stand up, maintain a sitting position, eat) (fig. 3). The study showed that aPTT was prolonged by approximately 1.5 times and that FPA

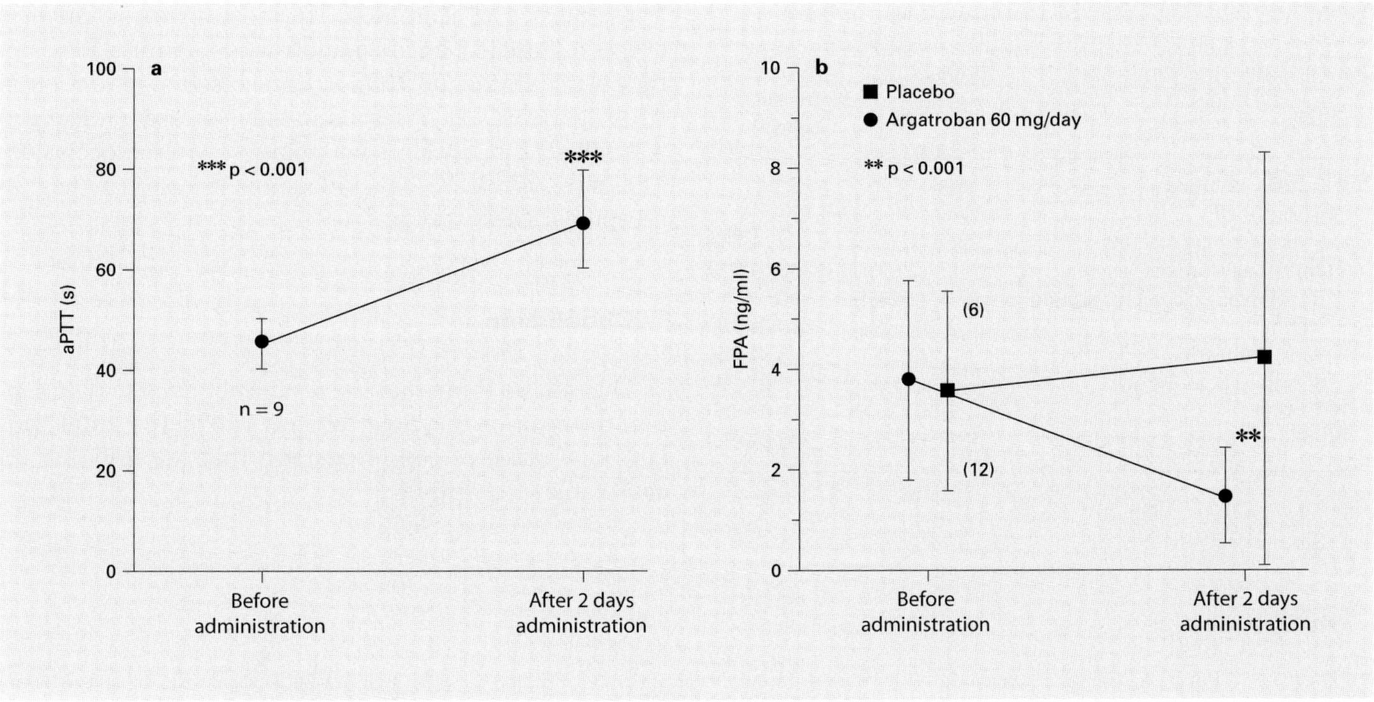

Fig. 4. Effect of a 120-mg continuous drip infusion of argatroban for 48 h on aPTT (**a**) and FPA (**b**) (means ± SD) in acute cerebral thrombosis. The number of cases is shown in parentheses. From Tanaka et al. [19] (with slight modification).

levels, which were high before argatroban administration, were reduced to normal levels after drug administration [19] (fig. 4). The normalization of FPA levels following argatroban administration indicates that argatroban inhibited thrombin in the blood and improved the hypercoagulable state immediately after the onset of cerebral thrombosis. This activity may be linked to the subsequent symptomatic improvement.

Argatroban and Hemodialysis in AT-Deficient Patients or Patients with Decreased AT

Heparin is commonly used as an anticoagulant in hemodialysis. Heparin exerts its anticoagulant activity by promoting binding of thrombin and AT in the blood, so the antithrombotic activity of heparin is reduced in patients with <70% normal levels of blood AT activity. There have been reports that heparin does not produce the expected anticoagulant activity in AT-deficient patients or patients with decreased AT, especially in hemodialysis where clotting in the dialyzer makes hemodialysis extremely difficult to maintain [6]. In contrast to heparin, the anticoagulant action of argatroban does not involve AT and the drug can exhibit antithrombin activity and the resulting anticoagulant activity without exhausting AT. Argatroban was considered to have potential in patients with congenital or acquired AT deficiency, where hemodialysis proves extremely difficult with heparin treatment.

In patients where hemodialysis is extremely difficult with heparin treatment because of coagulation in the dialyzer, argatroban administered within the dialysis circuit at 12–48 mg/h through continuous drip infusion was confirmed as effective in preventing clotting in the dialyzer [6].

Argatroban and Post-Marketing Surveillance Safety Information in Japan

Table 1 shows the summarized results of post-marketing surveillance safety information of argatroban in Japan. During a five-year period there were approximately 3,800 cases on each indication of acute cerebral thrombosis or chronic arterial occlusion treated with argatroban.

Table 1. Post-marketing surveillance of argatroban in Japan

Survey items	Stroke	Chronic arterial occlusion
Institutions included	590	620
Cases examined	3,777	3,791
Cases with adverse reactions	386 (10.2%)	178 (4.7%)
Hemorrhagic adverse events	77 (2.0%)	33 (0.9%)
Hemorrhagic cerebral infarction	44 (1.2%)	0
Hematuria	12 (0.3%)	10 (0.3%)
Gastrointestinal hemorrhage	5 (0.1%)	3 (0.1%)
Cerebral hemorrhage	3 (0.1%)	2 (0.1%)
Others	13 (0.3%)	18 (0.5%)
Nonhemorrhagic adverse events	309 (8.2%)	145 (3.8%)

These cases were examined. The most significant adverse events for argatroban are hemorrhagic complications, but they were infrequent. Hemorrhagic cerebral infarction in stroke patients was observed in only 44 cases (1.2%) and was not seen in patients with chronic arterial occlusion. Therefore, we have concluded that argatroban has an acceptable safety profile.

Conclusion

Overall, we think that the results obtained to date support the position that argatroban is an effective anticoagulant in a range of conditions and that the drug has an acceptable safety profile.

References

1 Okamoto S, Hijikata A, Kinjo K, Kikumoto R, Ohkubo K, Tonomura S, Tamao Y: A novel series of synthetic thrombin-inhibitors having extremely potent and highly selective action. Kobe J Med Sci 1975;21:43–51.
2 Okamoto S, Hijikata A, Kikumoto R, Tonomura S, Hara H, Ninomiya K, Maruyama A, Sugano M, Tamao Y: Potent inhibition of thrombin by the newly synthesized arginine derivative No. 805 The importance of stereostructure of its hydrophobic carboxamide portion. Biochem Biophys Res Commun 1981;101:440–446.
3 Nagasawa H, Fukutake K, Hada M, Takahashi E, Matsubara Y, Samori T, Ikematsu S, Kitahara T, Ukita M, Fujimaki M, Fukutake K: Phase one study of synthetic antithrombin agent (MD-805). Single and multiple administration studies. Jpn J Clin Pharmacol 1981;12:359–375.
4 Berry CN, Girardot C, Lecoffre C, Lunven C: Effects of the synthetic thrombin inhibitor argatroban on fibrin- or clot-incorporated thrombin: Comparison with heparin and recombinant hirudin. Thromb Haemost 1994:72:381–386.
5 Kumada T, Abiko Y: Comparative study on heparin and a synthetic thrombin inhibitor III-deficient animals. Thromb Res 1981;24:285–298.
6 Ohta K, Koshikawa S, Hirasawa S, Mitsuno K, Hibi I, Sawada K, Sakai R, Matsuo T: Effectiveness of MD-805 (argatroban) in hemodialysis patients with antithrombin III deficiency. New Drugs Clin 1992;41:971–983.
7 Warkentin TE: Heparin-induced thrombocytopenia: A clinicopathologic syndrome. Thromb Haemost 1999;82:439–447.
8 Maruyama S: Synthetic anticoagulant. Jpn J Clin Hematol 1990;31:776–781.
9 Nakamura K, Hatano Y, Mori K: Thrombin-induced vasocontriction in isolated cerebral arteries and the influence of a synthetic thrombin inhibitor. Thromb Res 1985;40:715–720.
10 Tamao Y, Yamamoto T, Kikumoto R, Hara H, Itoh J, Hirata T, Mineo K, Okamoto S: Effect of a selective thrombin inhibitor MCI-9038 on fibrinolysis in vitro and in vivo. Thromb Haemost 1986;56:28–34.
11 Tamao Y, Yamamoto T, Hirata T, Kinugasa M, Kikumoto R: Effect of argatroban on blood coagulation. Jap J Pharm Ther 1986;14:7–12.
12 Fukutake K, Tateyama M, Amano K, Ueda M, Fujimaki M: Clinical pharmacology of argatroban, selective anti-thrombin agent: Comparative study with heparin. Cardioangiology 1991; 29:190–196.
13 Tanabe T, Yasuda K, Mishima Y, Furukawa K, Sakaguchi S, Kamiya K, Shionoya S, Katsumura T, Kusaba A, Sakuma A: Therapeutic effect of argatroban (MD-805), a thrombin inhibitor, on chronic arterial occlusion. A comparative study with ticlopidine by a double-blind study. Cardioangiology 1987;22:185–202.
14 Itoh K, Ohgi S, Tanaka K, Tsujimoto M, Hara H, Mori T: The effect of MD 805, synthetic thrombin inhibitor, on peripheral circulation. Geka Shinryou (Tokyo) 1987;29:122–126.
15 Akahori M, Chishiro T, Tanaka T: Clinical discussion on the dose effect of argatroban in arteriosclerosis obliterans (ASO) – Especially coagulation and fibrinolysis marker Jpn J Med Pharm Sci 1993;30:409–405.
16 Sampaolo S, Cervos-Navarro J, Djouchadar D, Figols J: Clinical and experimental evidence of microthrombosis in cerebral ischemia; in Hartmann A, Wuschinesky (eds): Cerebral Ischemia and Hemorrheology. Berlin, Springer, 1987, pp 386–393.
17 Chao-Hung H, Han-Hwa H, Wen-Jang W: The serial hemostasis-related changes in patients with cerebral infarction: Comparison between progressing and non-progressing stroke. Thromb Res 1989;55:635–647.
18 Kobayashi S, Tazaki Y: Effect of the thrombin inhibitor Argatroban in acute cerebral thrombosis. Semin Thromb Hemost 1997;23:531–534.
19 Tanaka Y, Kawabata S, Sin R, Takatsuka K, Nishikawa H, Yoshikawa N, Komatsu T: Therapeutic effect of argatroban (MD-805), antithrombin agent, in the acute stage of cerebral thrombosis. J Clin Ther Med 1987;3:133–142.

Pathophysiology of Haemostasis and Thrombosis

Pathophysiol Haemost Thromb 2002;32(suppl 3):29–35
DOI: 10.1159/000069106

Current Perspective on Antithrombin Drugs

John L. McGregor

Inserm Unit 331, Faculty of Medicine, RTH Laénnec, University of Lyon 1, Lyon, France

Key Words
Thrombin inhibition · Protease-activated receptor · Thrombin-receptor-activated protease · Crescentic glomerular nephritis · Renal inflammation

Abstract
Thrombin is a multifunctional serine protease, which is involved in blood coagulation and thrombosis, inflammation and wound repair in tissue injury. Its role in the amelioration of inflammatory tissue injury has been investigated. Protease-activated cell surface receptors (PARs) when activated by thrombin result in the production of proinflammatory mediators. In the kidney, these PARs are expressed on the glomerular epithelium and the vascular endothelium. The significant impact of thrombin inhibition on the development of crescentic glomerular nephritis is discussed.

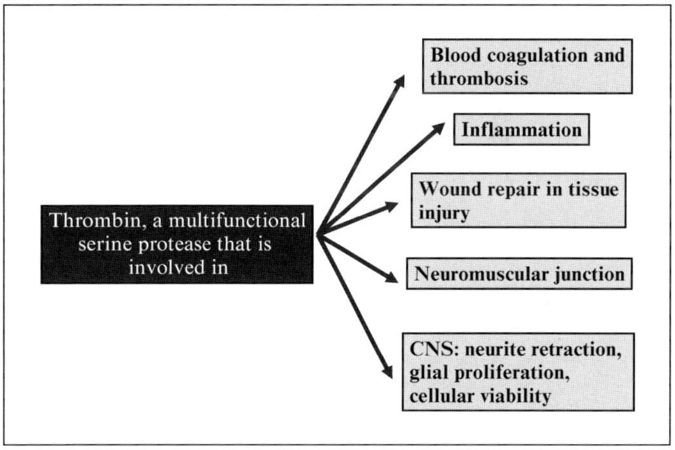

Fig. 1. Processes in which thrombin is involved.

The following is a brief overview on the potential use of anti-thrombin drugs in new therapeutic areas, distinct from their established use in thromboembolic disorders.

Thrombin

Thrombin is a serine protease involved in the functioning of a variety of physiological processes, e.g. blood coagulation and thrombosis, inflammation, wound repair in tissue injury, neuromuscular junction activity and, in the central nervous system, neurite retraction, glial proliferation and cellular viability (fig. 1).

Thrombin exerts its effect on both circulating cells and on those in the endothelium of the blood vessels (fig. 2, 3). Platelets are activated to aggregate and synthesise thromboxanes; leucocytes become chemotactic with cytokine production and lymphocytes undergo mitogenesis. In the vessel wall, the influence of thrombin on endothelial cells is to induce activation and expression of cell adhesion molecules (CAM) such as P and E selectins. In addition, chemokines and autacoids are expressed; and smooth muscle vasoconstriction occurs.

KARGER
Fax + 41 61 306 12 34
E-Mail karger@karger.ch
www.karger.com

1424–8832/02/0329–0029$18.50/0

Accessible online at:
www.karger.com/pht

John L. McGregor, PhD, Dr. B.H.
Director of Functional Genomics, Thrombosis Research Institute
Emmanuel Kaye Building, Manresa Road, Chelsea
UK–London SW3 6LR (England)
Tel. +44 20 7351 8314, Fax +44 20 7351 8317, E-Mail mcgregor@tri-london.ac.uk

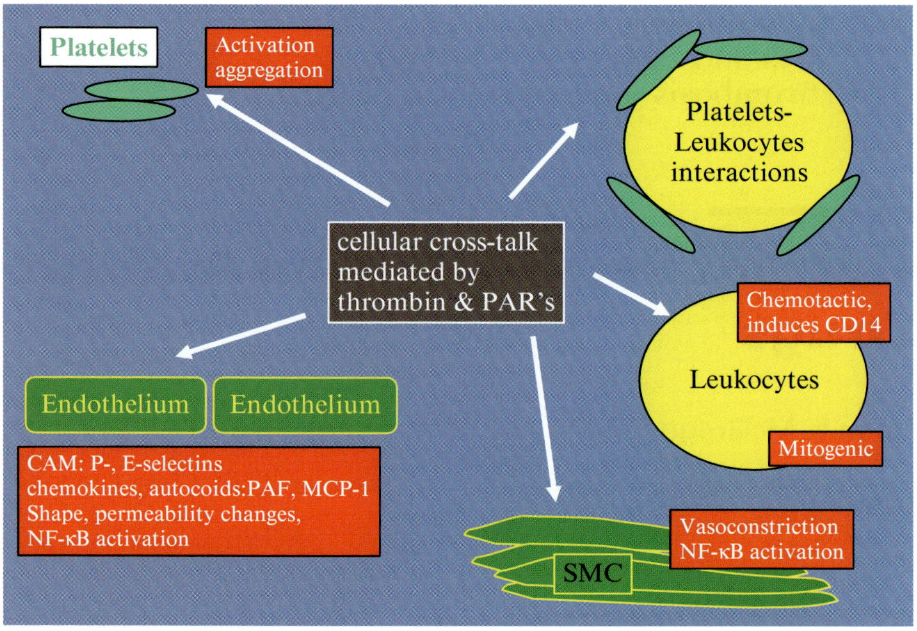

Fig. 2. Effects of thrombin on circulating and endothelial cells.

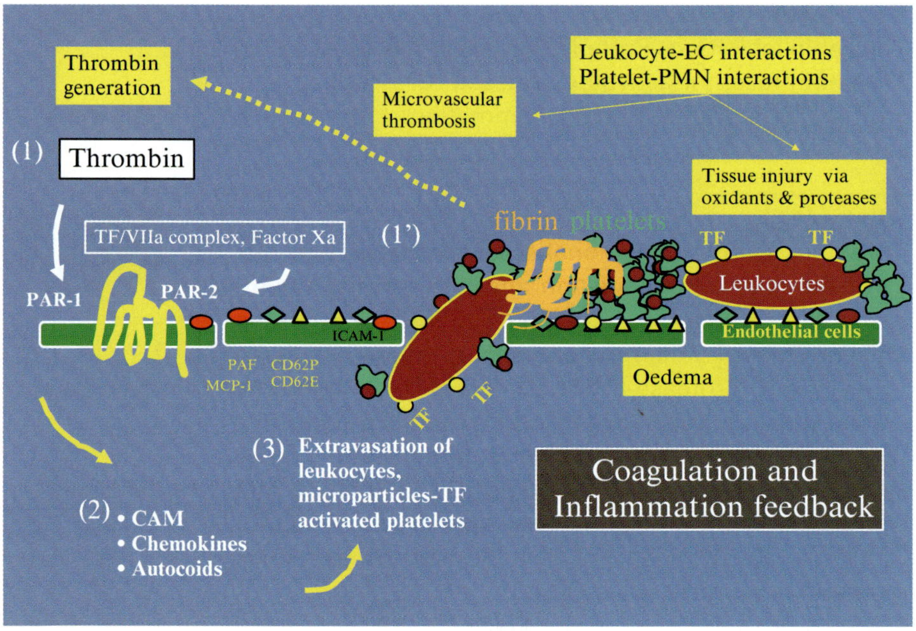

Fig. 3. Thrombin involvement in inflammatory pathways.

These events are brought about via cleavage of thrombin with cell surface protease receptors which become activated (PARs). This mechanism of action affords an understanding of the relationship between the inflammatory and coagulation processes. Thrombin cleaves with PAR-1 and VIIa complex and factor Xa cleave with PAR-2. The presence, together, on the endothelium of activated CAMs with associated selectins leads to leucocyte migration and extravasation. Micro-particles bearing tissue factor plus activated platelets can induce tissue injury. Platelets interacting together will produce microvascular thrombosis and oedema; interaction with leucocytes (PMN) may induce further thrombin generation.

These events make it reasonable to propose that inhibition of thrombin activity on PAR-1 would not only reduce thrombotic sequelae, but also the inflammatory process. The question can thus be asked: can one use as a potential therapeutic target for non-thromboembolic disorders the 'cellular cross-talk' mediated by thrombin and PARs?

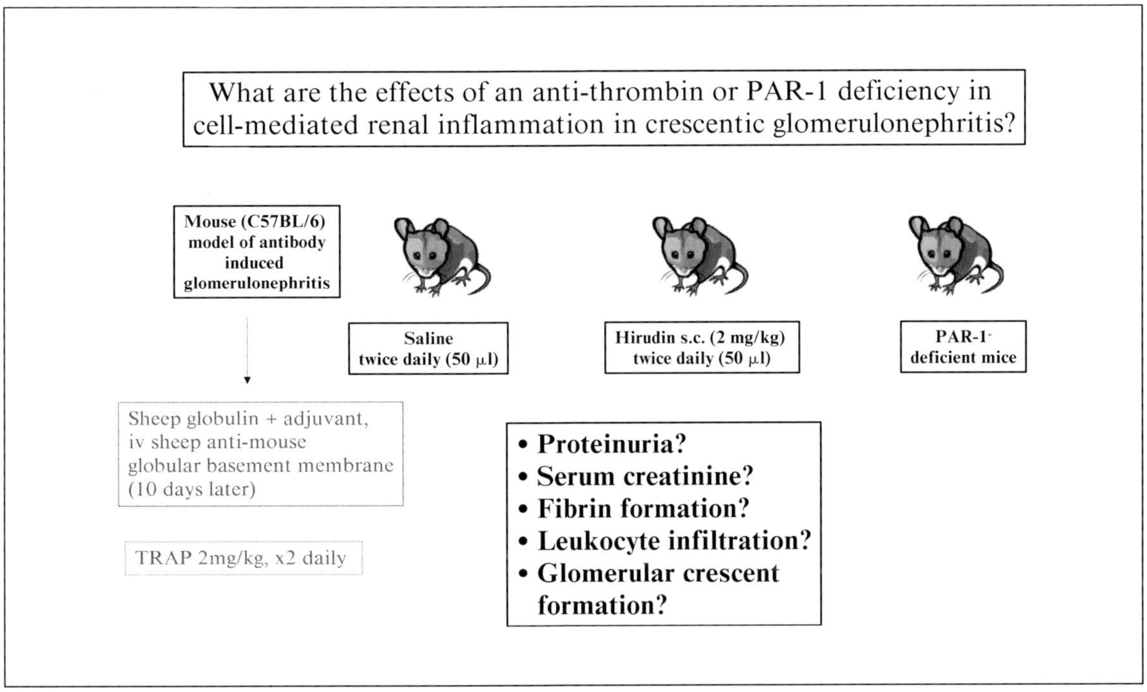

Fig. 4. Thrombin effect on PAR-1 murine model of crescentic GN. From Cunningham et al. [1].

PAR-1 and PAR-2 are expressed in the human kidney: PAR-1 on the glomerular epithelium and endothelium of the renal vasculature. As already stated, activation of PAR-1, by thrombin or thrombin receptor-activating peptides (TRAPs) in vitro, results in the production of pro-inflammatory mediators from the endothelium. Little is known about the direct pro-inflammatory effects of thrombin in vivo, but it is postulated that the cellular effects of serine proteases of the coagulation pathway may promote inflammatory glomerular injury.

Crescentic Glomerulonephritis

Glomerulonephritis (GN) is the most frequent cause of end stage renal failure. A particularly severe and rapidly progressive form of this disease is termed crescentic GN. It is characterised by inflammatory cell infiltration at the glomerular level, deposition of fibrin and upregulation of procoagulant molecules. Furthermore, upregulation of PAR-1 messenger RNA is associated with a down-regulation of PAR-1 antigen (fig. 4).

The contribution of thrombin and PAR-1 to inflammatory renal injury has been studied in vivo using a well-characterised murine model of crescentic GN [1]. Four groups of WT PAR-1 GKO mice were used. Each group was sensitised by nephritigenic antigen and sheep anti-mouse glomerular basement membrane globulin to develop glomerulonephritis (fig. 4). One group of mice received normal saline as a control, one group received hirudin to selectively inhibit the serine protease activity of thrombin, one group was PAR-1 deficient and the control group and the PAR-1-deficient mice received, in addition, TRAP, so forming the fourth group.

All mice were treated as above and after 10 days the following parameters were recorded: development of crescentic GN, proteinurea, serum creatinine, fibrin formation, leucocyte infiltration and glomerular crescent formation. Pathology from stained kidney samples was carried out on the four groups of mice to investigate presence of renal tissue damage (fig. 5–7).

It was shown that thrombin is an important mediator of injury in crescentic GN.

Those mice receiving hirudin and those that were PAR-1 deficient exhibited lower levels of proteinurea, serum creatinine, crescent formation, leucocyte and T-cell macrophage infiltration and fibrin deposition. Hirudin, through its blocking action on PAR-1 activity of thrombosis, afforded significant protection from the development of crescentic GN. PAR-1 deficiency protects against de-

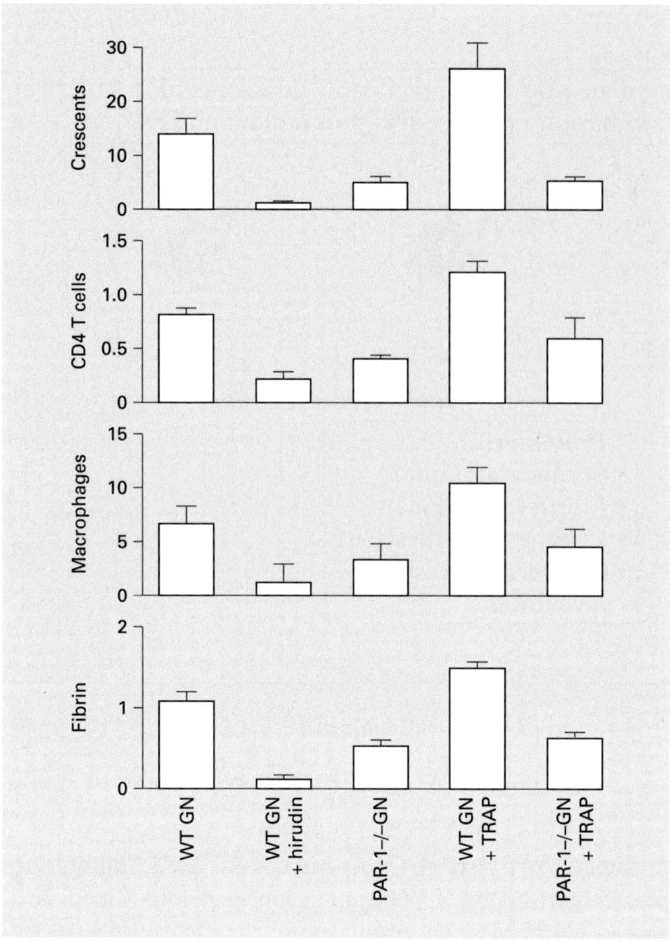

5

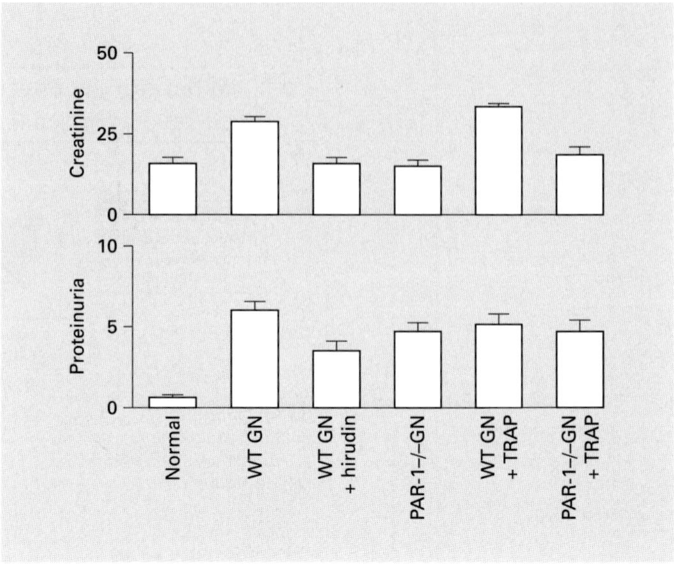

6

Fig. 5. Effect of thrombin on fibrin, white cells, T cells and crescents in murine model of crescentric GN. From Cunningham et al. [1].
Fig. 6. Effect of thrombin on proteinurea and creatinine in murine model of crescentic GN. From Cunningham et al. [1].

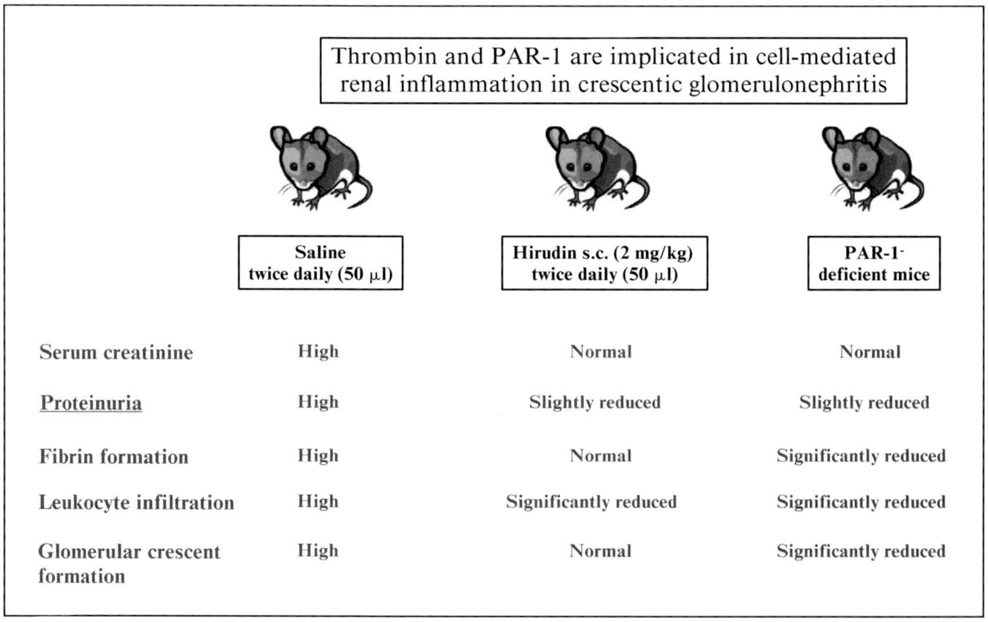

Fig. 7. Involvement of thrombin and PAR-1 in cell-mediated renal inflammation in crescentic GN. From Cunningham et al. [1].

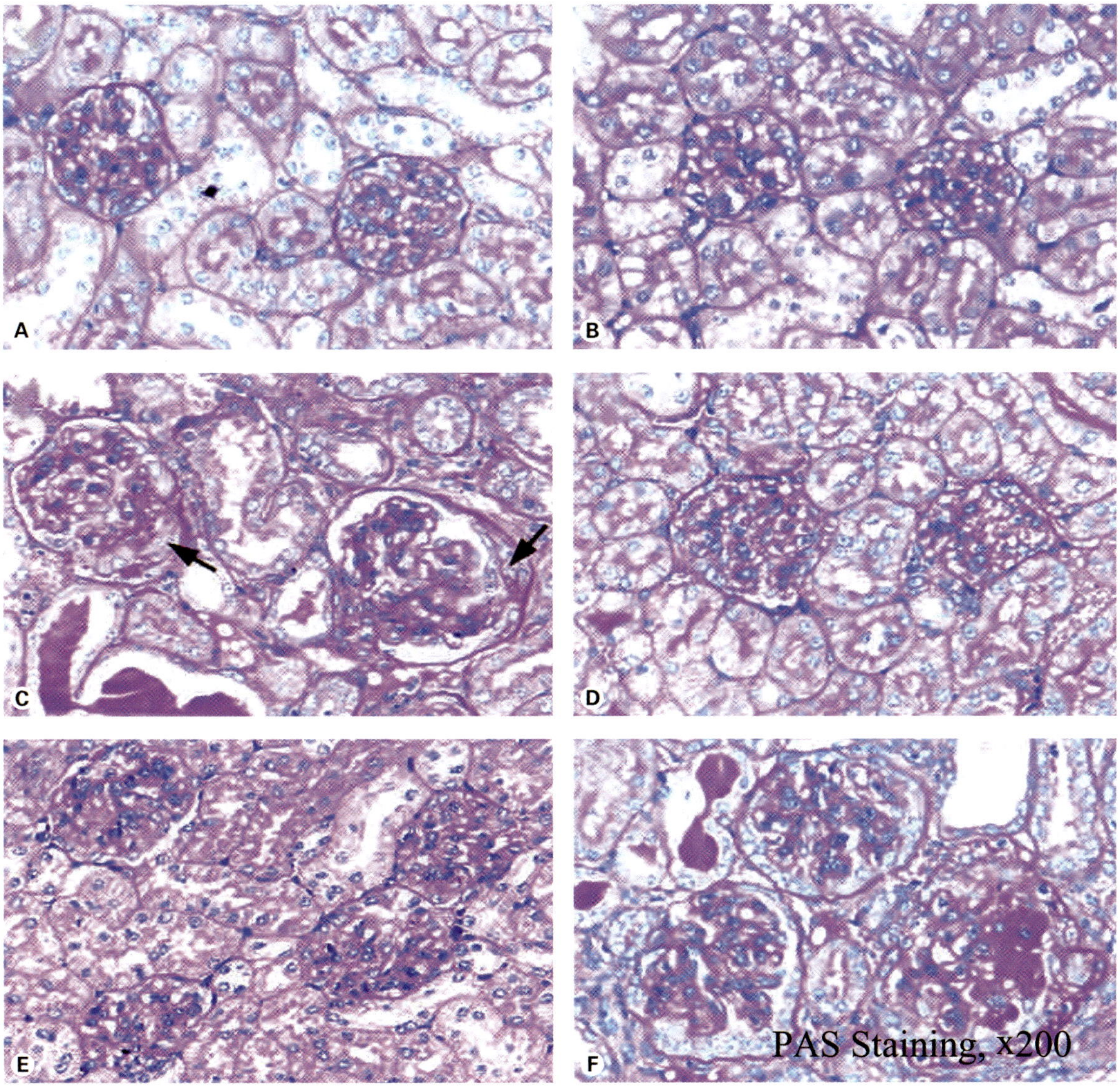

Fig. 8. Effects of thrombin and PAR-1 on glomerular pathology in crescentic GN. From Cunningham et al. [1]. PAS. × 200. **A** Glomeruli, control before GN. **B** Glomeruli in PAR-1-deficient mice before GN. **C** Following 10 days of GN: proliferative changes in glomerular tufts: crescents, Bowman's space. **D** Size of glomeruli following 10 days of GN + hirudin. **E** Following 10 days of GN in PAR-1-deficient mice. **F** Following 10 days of GN + TRAP.

velopment of crescentic GN (64% decrease compared with controls).

TRAP given to the control mice increased the levels of these parameters.

Microscopic examination of stained kidney sections showed the following (fig. 8):

A glomeruli before induction of GN are normal;
B glomeruli from PAR-1-deficient mice before induction of GN are normal;
C glomeruli from normal controls 10 days after initiation of GN show proliferative changes in the glomerular tufts and crescents in Bowman's capsule;
D crescentic glomerular injury is markedly diminished by hirudin treatment, although there are still some proliferative changes present;
E PAR-1-deficient mice show marked attenuation of crescentic GN following induction, and
F administration of TRAP accentuates crescentic GN injury.

9

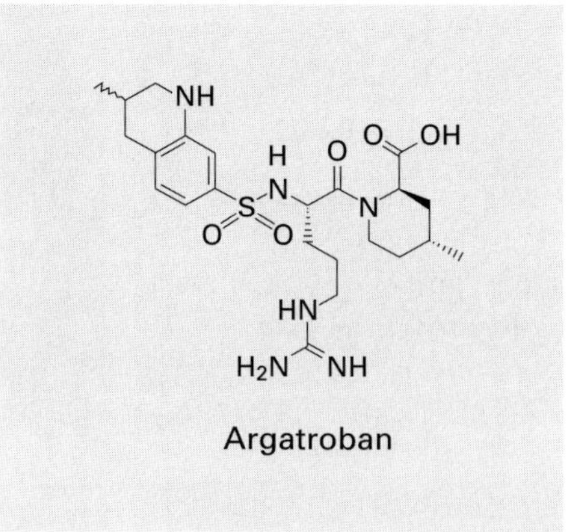

10

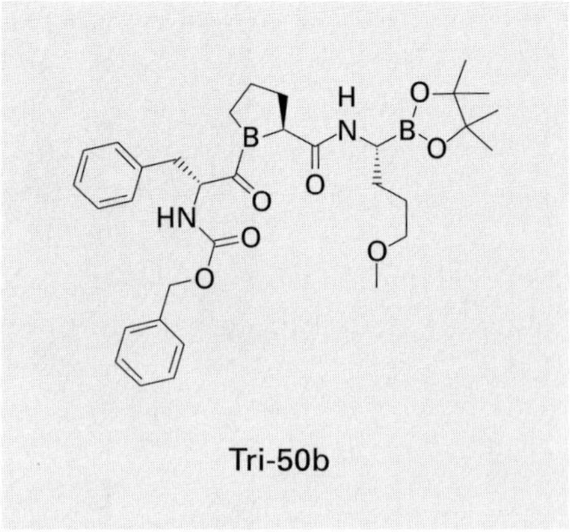

Fig. 9. Argatroban. From ref. 2.
Fig. 10. Tri-50b. From ref. 2.

11

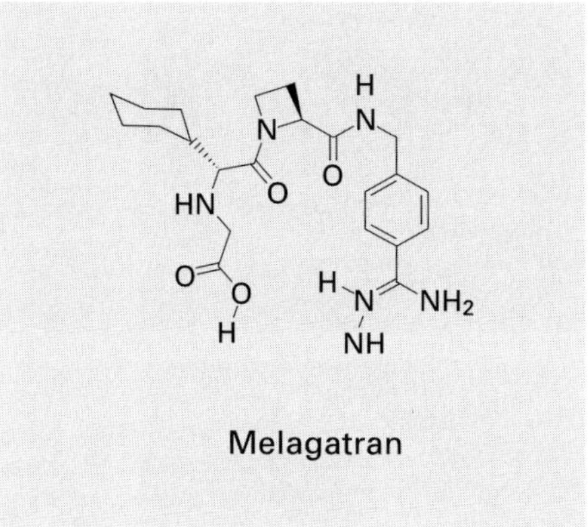

12

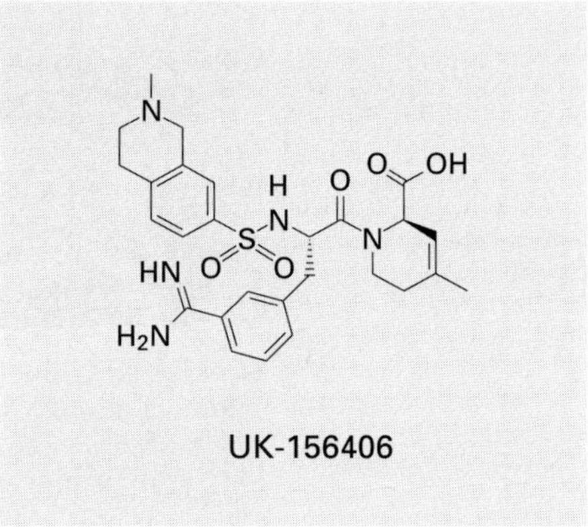

Fig. 11. Melagatran. From ref. 2.
Fig. 12. UK-156406. From ref. 2.

The protective effects of hirudin in this murine model of crescentic GN demonstrate a pivotal pro-inflammatory role for thrombin in the development of inflammatory renal injury. It demonstrates the important contribution of direct cellular effects of procoagulant molecules to inflammatory tissue injury. However, it should be noted that the therapeutic effect of hirudin in reducing renal injury in crescentic GN is not complete. The PAR-1 deficiency data show the importance of this receptor, independent of fibrinogen cleavage or other coagulation factors in the development of renal injury. The TRAP data further confirm the role of PAR-1 in inflammatory-cell-mediated disease.

Potential Antithrombin Molecules for Use in Certain Types of Inflammatory Diseases

The mouse study described indicates that direct inhibition of thrombin PAR-1 cleavage could play an important role in the therapy of some inflammatory diseases.

Argatroban, a Mitsubishi Chemical Industries molecule (Ki of 38 n*M* for human thrombin) (fig. 9), is a reversible direct inhibitor of thrombin, has a short half-life (39–51 min in man), has multiple targets, is non-antigenic and is cleared primarily by the hepatic system.

It is currently available in the USA and Canada (marketed by GlaxoSmithKline) and Korea (marketed by Mitsubishi Pharma Corporation) for the treatment of heparin-induced thrombocytopenia (HIT). In Japan it is marketed by Mitsubishi Pharma Corporation for a number of thrombotic disorders. It could potentially be used in most indications where intravenous heparin is (presently) used.

Some of the new generation of potential thrombin inhibitors, in preclinical development, are claimed to show significant oral bioavailability. A majority of these compounds can be classified as non-electrophilic inhibitors. In clinical development a number of compounds are currently being tested. Tri-50b (fig. 10) is currently in phase II. It is also directed towards arterial and venous thrombosis. It acts as a fast-binding competitive inhibitor when compared to S18326 and DuP714. Efegatran (LY-2944468) (Eli Lilly) has been tested in patients with unstable angina and in thrombolytic therapy and showed similar efficacy to heparin (a second molecule from Eli Lilly is currently in phase I as an oral anti-thrombin inhibitor). Melagatran (Astra-Zeneca) (fig. 11) is a non-electrophilic inhibitor and is in phase III trials for stroke prevention following atrial fibrillation and in deep vein thrombosis. Beneficial effects of melagatran were observed in renal function and systemic haemodynamics in endotoxaemic pigs with septic shock. Improvement over LMW heparin enoxaparin and heparin in deep vein thrombosis after hip replacement surgery was observed with desirudin (CGP39393, Novartis), a recombinant hirudin.

One of the thrombin inhibitors in clinical development (fig. 12), UK-156406, is an analogue of argatroban and has aroused interest in the treatment of lung fibrosis. Indeed, PARs have been implicated by their role in lung fibrosis. Use of UK-156406 in lung fibrosis suggests that thrombin inhibitors could equally be used as therapeutic tools in areas other than blood coagulation and platelet aggregation.

Conclusion

Increasing evidence shows that thrombin and PARs are linked to certain types of inflammatory diseases. Thrombin inhibitors may potentially represent a new generation of drugs for the treatment of certain inflammatory disorders, e.g. renal inflammation in crescentic GN.

References

1. Cunningham MA, Rondeau E, Chen X, Coughlin SR, Holdsworth SR, Tipping PG: Protease-activated receptor 1 mediates thrombin-dependent, cell-mediated renal inflammation in crescentic glomerulonephritis. J Exp Med 2000;191:455–561.
2. Steinmetzer T, Hauptmann J, Sturzebecker J: Advances in the development of thrombin inhibitors. Exp Opin Invest Drugs 2001;10:845–864.

Pathophysiology of Haemostasis and Thrombosis

Pathophysiol Haemost Thromb 2002;32(suppl 3):36–38
DOI: 10.1159/000069107

Clinical Results with Direct Thrombin Inhibitors

Andrew N. Nicolaides

Cyprus Institute of Neurology and Genetics, Nicosia, Cyprus, and Imperial College of Science Technology and Medicine, London, UK

Key Words
Direct thrombin inhibitors · Hirudin

Abstract
Direct thrombin inhibitors inactivate thrombin without the need for antithrombin and some inactivate not only thrombin but also fibrin-bound thrombin. Hirudin has been shown to be more effective than low-dose unfractionated heparin and low molecular weight heparin for the prevention of deep vein thrombosis in high-risk orthopaedic patients. Major studies are assessing the value of direct thrombin inhibitors in patients with acute coronary syndromes. Currently, argatroban is the drug of choice in patients with heparin-induced thrombocytopenia.

Introduction

The established anticoagulant agents, unfractionated heparin, oral anticoagulants and aspirin are effective, but have limitations. Unfractionated heparin has a narrow therapeutic window and a variable dose response because it binds with plasma proteins and proteins released from platelets. The effect of oral anticoagulants such as warfarin is also erratic. Thus, both require monitoring. In addition, unfractionated heparin is unable to inactivate thrombin bound to fibrin [1] and factor Xa bound to activated platelets trapped within the thrombus [2]. These enzymes may cause thrombus growth once treatment is stopped. Another disadvantage is the development of heparin-induced thrombocytopenia.

The above limitations have stimulated the search for newer antithrombotic drugs and advances in biotechnology and molecular biology have made possible the development of low molecular weight (LMW) heparin and direct thrombin inhibitors, which have a predictable dose response. Also, the limitations of aspirin whose effect is based on the inhibition of thromboxane A_2 synthesis have been overcome by the development of new platelet inhibitors which inhibit ADP-induced platelet activation (ticlopidine, clopidogrel) or glycoprotein IIb/IIIa antagonists which block platelet aggregation in response to all agonists.

The aim of this review is to summarize the development and clinical potential of direct thrombin inhibitors.

Properties of Direct Thrombin Inhibitors

Direct thrombin inhibitors inactivate thrombin without the need for antithrombin to be present. In addition they inactivate thrombin bound to fibrin and thrombomodulin [1, 3]. In contrast to unfractionated heparin, they are not neutralized by platelet factor 4 (PF4), they do not bind to plasma proteins and as a consequence. They have a predictable anticoagulant response. Another advantage is that they do not cause immunologically mediated thrombocytopenia.

KARGER
Fax +41 61 306 12 34
E-Mail karger@karger.ch
www.karger.com

1424–8832/02/0329–0036$18.50/0

Accessible online at:
www.karger.com/pht

Prof. Andrew N. Nicolaides, Chairman
Cyprus Institute of Neurology and Genetics
P.O. Box 23462
CY–1683 Nicosia (Cyprus)
Tel. +44 357 22 358 600, Fax +44 357 22 358 237/8, E-Mail anicolai@mdrtc.cing.ac.cy

Direct Thrombin Inhibitors in Clinical Use

Hirudin is the oldest known direct thrombin inhibitor. It is a 65-amino-acid polypeptide initially isolated from the saliva of medicinal leeches, but is now produced by recombinant DNA technology (lepirudin/desirudin). Bivalirudin (previously known as hirulog) is an LMW synthetic 20-amino-acid polypeptide. Both bind to thrombin at exosite 1 (the substrate recognition site) and to the active site. By inactivating not only thrombin but also fibrin-bound thrombin they inhibit thrombin-induced platelet activation. Other LMW preparations binding only to the active site are argatroban, efegatran, inogatran and melagatran.

H376/95 is the prodrug form of melagatran, which can be given orally. It is a small molecule (MW = 474) rapidly absorbed, producing peak levels in 15–30 min with melagatran peak levels of 1–2 h. It has a bioavailability of 20% and a predictable dose response.

Efficacy in the Prevention of Deep Vein Thrombosis

In a randomized controlled phase 3 clinical trial, hirudin was found to be more effective than LMW heparin for the prevention of DVT in high-risk orthopedic patients [4]. The oral form (H376/95) of melagatran has been shown to be more effective in the prevention of venous thromboembolism (odds ratio 0.45) than dalteparin in patients having hip and knee replacement (The METHRO II study).

Effect on Restenosis following Coronary Angioplasty

In a study by Serruys et al. [5], 1,141 patients undergoing coronary angioplasty were randomized to hirudin or unfractionated heparin. Hirudin reduced the early (96-hour) cardiac events from 11% in the unfractionated heparin group to 5.5% in the hirudin group (p = 0.023). However, there was no difference in the event-free survival at 7 months.

Effect in Patients with Acute Coronary Syndromes

A number of moderate-sized studies using direct thrombin inhibitors in patients who were and were not receiving thrombolytic therapy were performed in the 1990s. They suggested that direct thrombin inhibitors were safe, had dose-dependent anticoagulation efficacy and improved angiographic findings [7–15].

On the basis of these findings three large subsequent studies tested hirudin against unfractionated heparin (GUSTO IIb, 1996; OASIS-1, 1997; OASIS-2, 1999) [16–18] in patients with non-ST-segment elevation acute coronary syndromes. There were 503 patients in GUSTO II b, 909 in OASIS-1 and 10,141 in OASIS-2. Pooled analysis of these three studies demonstrated that the risk of death at 7 days was reduced by 28% in the hirudin group but there was no difference at 35 days. In the OASIS-2 study major bleeding was common with hirudin, although the numbers of life-threatening episodes and hemorrhagic strokes were similar.

The value of direct thrombin inhibitors as adjunctive therapy in patients with ST segment elevation treated with thrombolytic therapy was investigated in several large trials. Three trials using relatively high doses of hirudin (HIT, GUSTO IIa, TIMI 9a) [19–21] were stopped prematurely because of an unacceptably high incidence of intracranial hemorrhage. The TIMI 9a and the GUSTO IIa trials were redesigned as the TIMI 9b and GUSTO IIb comparing lower doses of hirudin with unfractionated heparin.

In the TIMI 9b, 3,002 patients were randomized to 5,000 IU heparin as a bolus followed by 1,000 IU/h intravenously or hirudin (desirudin) 0.1 mg/kg bolus followed by 0.1 mg/kg/h. Both regimens were given for 96 h. The composite rate of death, myocardial infarction and refractory angina was 11.9% in the unfractionated heparin group and 12.9% in the hirudin group. In the GUSTO IIb trial, death or myocardial infarction at 30 days was 11.3% in the heparin group and 9.9% in the hirudin group. The conclusion was that in both studies both regimens were equally effective [22].

Preliminary studies of other direct thrombin inhibitors as adjuvant therapy in patients receiving thrombolytic therapy have produced conflicting results [23–26]. The HERO-Acute MI study randomized 412 patients into 5,000 IU of unfractionated heparin as a bolus followed by 1,000 IU/h or hirulog (low dose) 0.125 mg/kg bolus followed by 0.25 mg/kg/h for the first 12 h and subsequently 0.125 mg/kg/h up to 60 h or hirulog (high dose) 0.25 mg/kg bolus followed by 0.5 mg/kg/h for 12 h and subsequently 0.25 mg/kg/h up to 60 h. The results indicated that the high dose of hirulog in combination with streptokinase achieved TIMI grade 3 coronary flow in a higher percentage of patients at 90–120 min (48 vs. 35%). At 35 days, a 20–30% reduction was observed in the incidence of death, MI and cardiogenic shock in the hirulog group, but it was not statistically significant. In view of this trend, the HERO-2 trial has been set up which is currently assessing clinical end points in 17,000 patients treated with streptokinase and randomized to adjunctive hirulog or heparin therapy.

More data are needed before direct antithrombin inhibitors can replace unfractionated heparin in patients having acute coronary syndromes. However, there is one area in which direct thrombin inhibitors have an important place. Argatroban has become the drug of choice for patients with heparin-induced thrombocytopenia. In a large scale, non-randomized, prospective trial, argatroban reduced a combined end point of morbidity and mortality when compared with historical controls without any increase in bleeding risk [26]. This is the topic of a later paper.

References

1 Weitz JI, Hudoba M, Massel D, Maraganore J, Hirsh J: Clot-bound thrombin is protected from inhibition by heparin-antithrombin III but is susceptible to inactivation by antithrombin III-dependent inhibitors. J Clin Invest 1990;86:385–391.
2 Hirsh J: Heparin. N Engl J Med 1991;324: 1565–574.
3 Stone SR, Hofsteenge J: Kinetics of inhibition of thrombin by hirudin. Biochem 1986;25: 4622–4628.
4 Eriksson BI, Wille-Jorgensen P, Kalebo P, et al: A comparison of recombinant hirudin with a low-molecular-weight heparin to prevent thromboembolic complication after total hip replacement. N Engl J Med 1997;337:1329–1335.
5 Serruys PW, Herrman J-PR, Simon R, et al and the Helvetica Investigators: A comparison of hirudin with heparin in the prevention of restenosis after coronary angioplasty. N Engl J Med 1995;333:757–763.
6 Lidon RM, Theroux P, Juneau M, Adelman B, Maraganore J: Initial experience with a direct antithrombin, hirulog, in unstable angina: Anticoagulant, antithrombotic, and clinical effects. Circulation 1993;99;1495–1501.
7 Fox KA: r-Hirudin in unstable angina pectoris: Rationale and preliminary data from the APT pilot study. Eur Heart J 1995;16(suppl D):28–32.
8 Sharma GV, Lapsley D, Vita JA, Sharma S, Coccio E, Adelman B, Loscalzo J: Usefulness and tolerability of hirulog, a direct thrombin inhibitor, in unstable angina pectoris. Am J Cardiol 1993;72:1357–1360.
9 Fuchs J, Cannon CP, and the TIMI 7 Investigators: Hirulog in the treatment of unstable angina: Results of the Thrombin Inhibition in Myocardial Ischemia (TIMI) 7 Trial. Circulation 1995;92:727–733.
10 Topol EJ, Fuster V, Harrington RA, et al: Recombinant hirudin for unstable angina pectoris: A multicenter, randomized angiographic trial. Circulation 1994;89:1557–1566.
11 Lidon RM, Théroux P, Lespérance J, Adelman B, Bonan R, Duval D, Levesque J: A pilot, early angiographic patency study using a direct thrombin inhibitor as adjunctive therapy to streptokinase in acute myocardial infarction. Circulation 1994;89:1567–1572.
12 Théroux P, Perez-Villa F, Waters D, Lespérance J, Shabani F, Bonan R: Randomized double-blind comparison of two doses of hirulog with heparin as adjunctive therapy to streptokinase to promote early patency of the infarct-related artery in acute myocardial infarction. Circulation 1995;91:2132–2139.
13 Cannon CP, McCabe CH, Henry TD, et al: A pilot trial of recombinant desulfatohirudin compared with heparin in conjunction with tissue-type plasminogen activator and aspirin for acute myocardial infarction: Results of the Thrombolysis in Myocardial Infarction (TIMI) 5 trial. J Am Coll Cardiol 1994;23:993–1003.
14 Lee LV: Initial experience with hirudin and streptokinase in acute myocardial infarction: Results of the Thrombolysis in Myocardial Infarction (TIMI) 6 trial. Am J Cardiol 1995;75: 7–13.
15 Global Use of Strategies to Open Occluded Coronary Arteries (GUSTO) IIb Investigators: A comparison of recombinant hirudin with heparin for the treatment of acute coronary syndromes. N Engl J Med 1996;335:775–782.
16 Organization to Assess Strategies for Ischemic Syndromes (OASIS) Investigators: Comparison of the effects of two doses of recombinant hirudin compared with heparin in patients with acute myocardial ischemia without ST elevation: A randomized trial. Circulation 1997;96:769–777.
17 Organisation to Access Strategies for Ischemic Syndromes (OASIS-2) Investigators: Effects of recombinant hirudin (lepirudin) compared with heparin of death, myocardial infarction, refractory angina, and revacularisation procedures in patients with acute myocardial ischaemia without ST elevation: A randomised trial. Lancet 1999;353:429–438.
18 Neuhaus KL, von Essen R, Tebbe U, et al: Safety observations from the pilot phase of the randomized r-Hirudin for Improvement of Thrombolysis (HIT-III) study: A study of the Arbeitsgemeinschaft Leitender Kardiologischer Krankenhausärzte. Circulation 1994;90: 1638–1642.
19 GUSTO IIa Investigators: Randomized trial of intravenous heparin versus recombinant hirudin for acute coronary syndromes. Circulation 1994;90:1631–1637.
20 Antman EM, for the TIMI 9A investigators: Hirudin in acute myocardial infarction. Safety report from the thrombolysis and thrombin inhibition in myocardial infarction (TIMI) 9A trial. Circulation 1994;90:1624–1630.
21 The Global Use of Strategies to Open Occluded Coronary Arteries (GUSTO) IIb Investigators. A comparison of recombinant hirudin with heparin for the treatment of acute coronary syndrome. N Engl J Med 1996;335:775–782.
22 Ferguson JJ: Meeting highlights: XIX Congress of the European Society of Cardiology. Circulation 1997;96:3818–3821.
23 Alderman EL: Results from late-breaking clinical trials sessions at ACC '98. J Am Coll Cardiol 1998;32:1–7.
24 Cody RJ: Results from late breaking clinical trials session at ACC '97. J Am Coll Cardiol 1997;30:1–7.
25 White HD, Aylward PE, Collins R, et al: Randomized, double-blind comparison of hirulog versus heparin in patients receiving streptokinase and aspirin for acute myocardial infarction (HERO). Circulation 1997;96:2155–2161.
26 Lewis BE, Wallis DE, Berkowitz SD, Matthai WH, Fareed J, Walenga JM, Bartholomew J, Sham R, Lemer RG, Zeigler ZR, Rustagi PK, Jang IK, Rifkin SD, Moran J, Hursting MJ, Kelton JG, for the ARG-911 Study Investigators: Argatroban Anticoagulant Therapy in Patients With Heparin-Induced Thrombocytopenia. Circulation 2001;103:1838–1843.

Pathophysiology of Haemostasis and Thrombosis

Pathophysiol Haemost Thromb 2002;32(suppl 3):39–45
DOI: 10.1159/000069108

Argatroban in Thrombotic Stroke

Marian P. LaMonte

Division of Emergency Medicine, University of Maryland School of Medicine, The Maryland Brain Attack Center, Baltimore, Md., USA

Key Words

Stroke · Cerebral blood flow · Cerebral ischemia · Thrombin · Argatroban

Abstract

Evidence for the potential use of direct thrombin inhibition in the treatment of acute stroke is reviewed. Reduction of secondary microthrombi and improved regional collateral cerebral blood flow is the proposed mechanism of action of thrombin inhibition for the treatment of cerebral ischemia. A clinical study in Japan found that argatroban administered within 48 h of stroke symptom onset is safe and effective in reducing neurological impairment due to ischemic stroke. The implications of further clinical studies are discussed.

Introduction

The common pathway in precerebral and cerebral arterial occlusion is the fibrin-rich platelet thromboembolism. There are two mechanisms speculated to be important in improving cerebral blood flow in the peri-ischemic penumbra in thromboembolic occlusion. The first targets the cellular aspect of clot formation by reduction in further platelet aggregation, and the second targets alterations in the balance of coagulation proteins by accelerating plasminogen conversion or inhibiting thrombin. Drug therapies such as aspirin, clopidogrel or a glycoprotein (GP) IIb/IIIa receptor antagonist such as abciximab are used to interfere with platelet aggregation and agents such as tPA and heparins are used to alter coagulation proteins. Argatroban is a selective and potent antithrombin, which directly blocks thrombin activity without the use of cofactor antithrombin. It also inhibits fibrin formation, platelet aggregation and vascular contraction. Because of these properties, argatroban may participate in both of these mechanisms to achieve the enhancement of cerebral collateral blood flow.

Prior Studies of Anticoagulation Therapy in Acute Cerebral Ischemia

A recent Cochrane review of anticoagulant therapy started within 2 weeks of ischemic stroke onset included 21 trials involving 23,427 patients [1]. Studies reviewed by the Cochrane collaborative included those in which multiple types of anticoagulants were tested including standard unfractionated heparin, low molecular weight (LMW) heparins, heparinoids, oral anticoagulants, and thrombin inhibitors. Results were disappointing in that there was no evidence that anticoagulation therapy reduced the odds of all-cause mortality or the odds of death

KARGER

Fax + 41 61 306 12 34
E-Mail karger@karger.ch
www.karger.com

1424–8832/02/0329–0039$18.50/0

Accessible online at:
www.karger.com/pht

Marian P. LaMonte, MD, MSN, Associate Professor of Neurology and Surgery
Division of Emergency Medicine, University of Maryland Medical Center
Department of Neurology, Room N4W46, 22 South Greene Street
Baltimore, MD 21201 (USA)
Tel. +1 410 328 6484, Fax +1 410 328 5899, E-Mail mlamonte@umm.edu

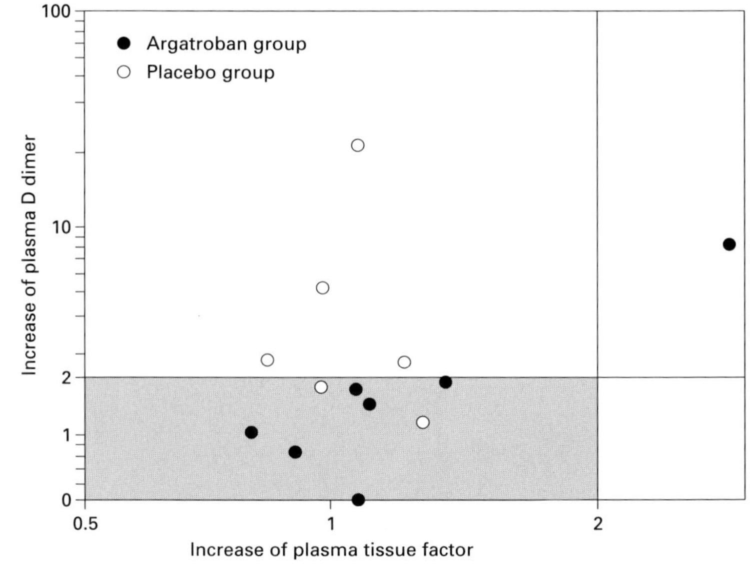

Fig. 1. Relationship between the D dimer and tissue factor levels in the acute phase of ischemic stroke. The values remain within twice that of baseline in argatroban-treated patients. From Kario et al. [7].

Table 1. Use of markers of platelet activation, coagulation and fibrinolysis in three classifications of acute ischemic stroke (from Uchiyama et al. [6])

Stroke type	Platelet activation	Coagulation	Fibrinolysis
Atherothrombotic			
Patients	+	+	+
Healthy controls	+	–	–
Cardioembolic	+	+	+
Lacunar	–	–	–

or dependency from stroke. In addition, the benefit of 9 fewer recurrent strokes per thousand was offset by an equal number of symptomatic intracranial hemorrhages. Similarly, a combined analysis of the CAST [2] and IST [3] trials concluded that the small gain in prevention of recurrent stroke was countered by the excess risk of intracranial hemorrhage in the anticoagulant-treated group [4]. The CAST and IST trials used aspirin and/or standard unfractionated heparin therapy. Because of a possible lower associated risk of hemorrhage with newer anticoagulants, a follow-up Cochrane review provided information on LMW heparins or heparinoids versus standard unfractionated heparin for acute ischemic stroke [5]. Five trials involving 705 patients treated within 2 weeks of ischemic stroke onset were included in this review. A significant benefit of prevention of deep vein thrombosis accrued to patients treated with LMW heparin or heparinoids as compared to those treated with unfractionated heparin. The number of major bleeding events was too small to provide a reliable estimate of risk, and no information was provided on recurrent stroke or functional outcome to provide a reliable estimate of benefit.

The newer generation anticoagulants, including synthetic direct-acting thrombin inhibitors, such as argatroban, and GP IIb/IIIa and factor Xa inhibitors, offer theoretical advantages over LMW and unfractionated heparins due to their more targeted inhibition of the coagulation cascade. Several clinical studies have been performed to explore the state of coagulation and fibrinolytic changes during ischemic stroke to advance the use of these more targeted therapies.

Studies of Coagulation and Fibrinolysis in Cerebral Ischemia

Using platelet activation, coagulation and fibrinolysis markers, Uchiyama et al. [6] attempted to profile such changes within specific ischemic stroke subtypes. Stroke types were classified according to the National Institute of

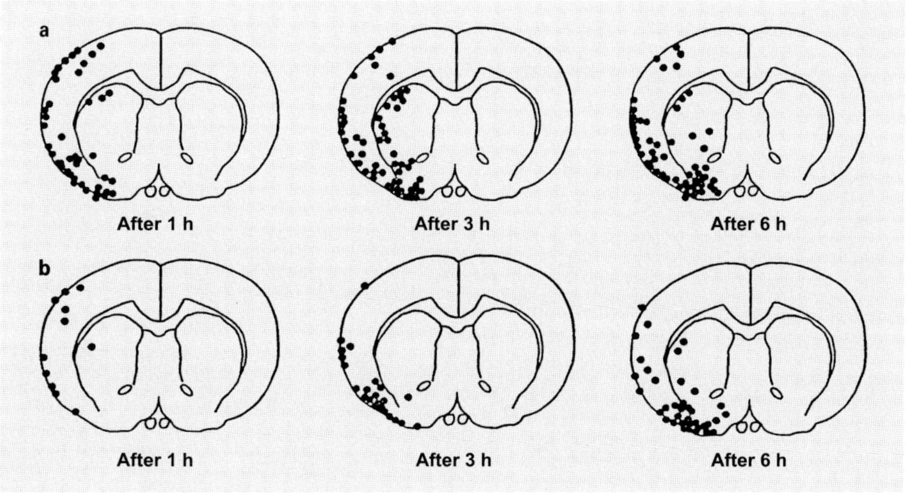

Fig. 2. Action of argatroban on incidence of microthrombi in rat brain. **a** Formation of secondary microthrombi in controls. **b** Formation of secondary microthrombi in argatroban (0.3 mg/h/rat)-treated rats. From Kawai et al. [8].

Neurological Disorders and Stroke (NINDS) Stroke Data Bank and included cardioembolic, atherothrombotic (separated into clinically stable or progressive subtypes), and lacunar. Clinical and laboratory testing of patients was performed to determine the category of cerebral infarction. Platelet function tests carried out were platelet aggregation, platelet activating factors (PAF), shear stress, platelet specific proteins, e.g. β-thromboglobulin and platelet factor 4 (PF4), platelet survival, lysis, accumulation, fibrinogen binding to platelet membrane and expression of P-selectin on platelet surfaces. Coagulation tests employed were antithrombin III, thrombin-antithrombin III complex (TAT) and fibrinopeptide A (FPA). Fibrinolysis markers were D dimer and plasma-α_2-plasmin inhibitor complex. All markers were assessed 7 days after onset of stroke.

Their study showed that marked platelet activation was seen in patients with either progressive or nonprogressive atherothrombotic strokes.

However, in patients with progressive strokes, coagulation and fibrinolysis were also observed.

Patients with cardioembolic strokes demonstrated marked fibrinolysis as well as platelet activation. Neither of these was seen in lacunar stroke possibly because there is not enough tissue damage in this stroke subtype (table 1).

Another study assessed D dimer and tissue factor levels as coagulation markers in acute ischemic stroke patients treated with either argatroban or placebo (fig. 1) [7]. Compared with baseline, the changes in values, 7 days after the acute episode, were less in the argatroban-treated patients and remained within twice the values on day 1.

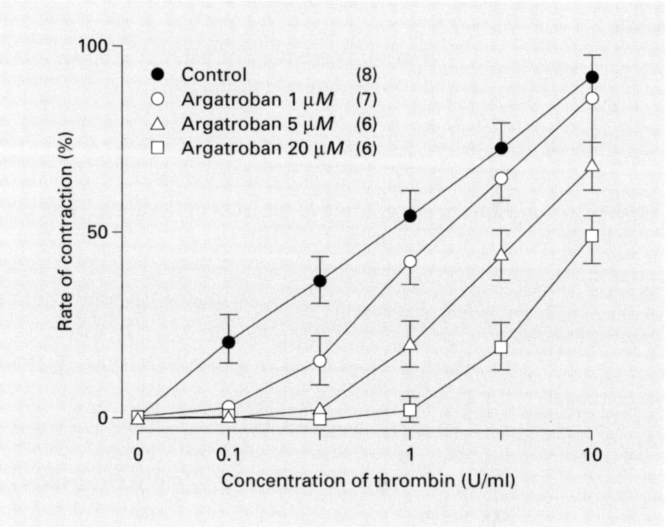

Fig. 3. Inhibitory effect of argatroban on dog basilar artery contraction.

Argatroban in Animal Models

The potential for argatroban to block microthrombus formation and artery smooth muscle contraction has been tested in animal models. Argatroban was administered using the rat middle cerebral artery occlusion model. At 1, 3 and 6 h following arterial occlusion, argatroban-treated animals showed significant reduction of secondary microthrombus formation in the brain (fig. 2) [8]. The inhibitory effect of argatroban on contraction of the isolated dog basilar artery was significant and showed a dose-dependent decrease in percentage rate of contraction following infusion of 0–10 U/ml of thrombin (fig. 3) [9].

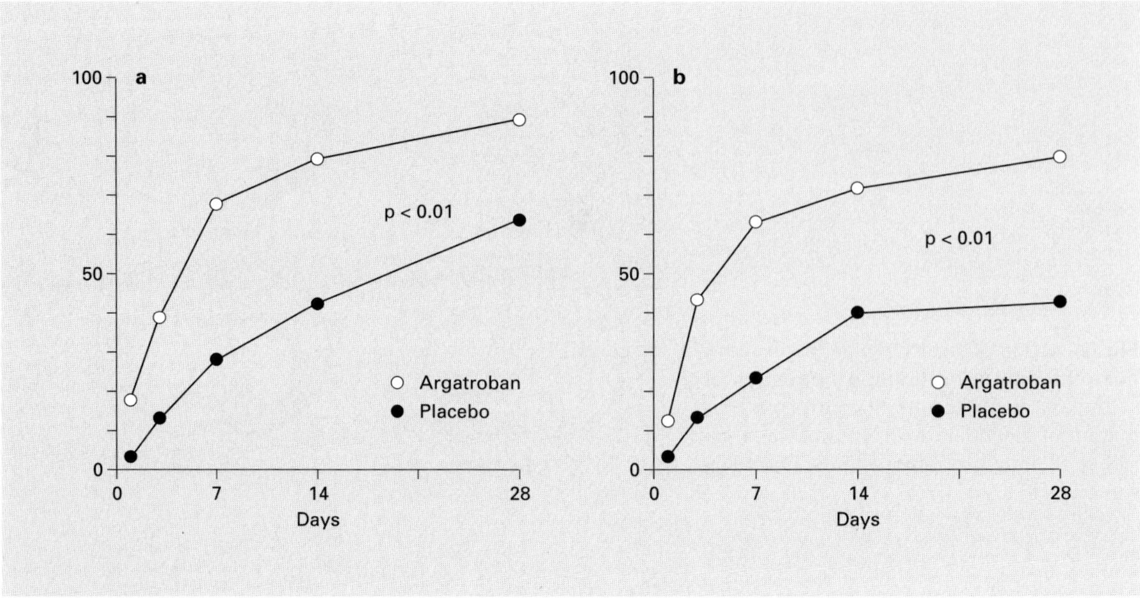

Fig. 4. Percentage of patients who showed more than one rank improvement. **a** ADL scale. **b** Paralyzed leg scale. From Kobayashi et al. [10].

Table 2. Global improvement rate of patients in the argatroban and placebo groups (from Kobayashi et al. [10])

	Total cases	Time from onset to administration	
		within 48 h	over 48 h
Argatroban	54.2% (59)	66.7% (30)	41.4% (29)
Placebo	23.7% (59)	22.6% (31)	25.0% (28)
Difference	30.5%	44.1%	16.4%
	Wilcoxon test ($p < 0.01$)	Wilcoxon test ($p < 0.01$)	Wilcoxon test NS

Figures in parentheses are numbers of cases. Average aPTT 48 h after initiation of argatroban: 1.53.

Argatroban in Clinical Trials

Some of the newer generation anticoagulants have been evaluated in advanced clinical trials of acute ischemic stroke. In Japan, argatroban has been tested in a multicenter, randomized, double-blind, placebo-controlled study of acute thrombotic stroke [10]. Fifty-two centers took part, recruiting a total of 119 patients. The protocol called for patients with thrombotic stroke to be randomized within 5 days of stroke onset to infusion of argatroban at 60 mg per day continuously for 48 h followed by a 20-mg intravenous infusion twice a day for 5 days versus placebo of sorbitol in a similar infusion. As a basic medication for patients in the acute stage, 500 ml glycerol was administered once daily for 7 days.

Inclusion criteria were all patients with large artery atherothrombotic stroke diagnosed by clinical and laboratory evaluation including brain CT. Exclusion criteria were hemorrhagic stroke, lacunar stroke and patients suspected of cardioembolic ischemic stroke.

The primary outcome of the study was evaluation of global improvement on day 28 following initiation of therapy. Patient rating scales employed on days 1, 3, 7, 14 and 28 included the Japan Coma Scale, the Subjective Symptom Scale and the Activity Daily Living scale (ADL). Other neurological evaluations for motor, sensory, visual fields, dysarthria, dysphagia, aphasia, anosognosia and level of consciousness were carried out on the same days. Global improvement was judged by the site investigators on the basis of results of rating scales devised for consciousness, motor and sensory findings, psychological symptoms and specific activities of daily living.

The results showed that the mean global improvement of patients at 28 days was statistically significant for the group of patients treated with argatroban within 48 h of stroke symptom onset compared to that of the control patients (table 2). Overall, there was a 54.2% mean improvement in the argatroban group of patients vs.

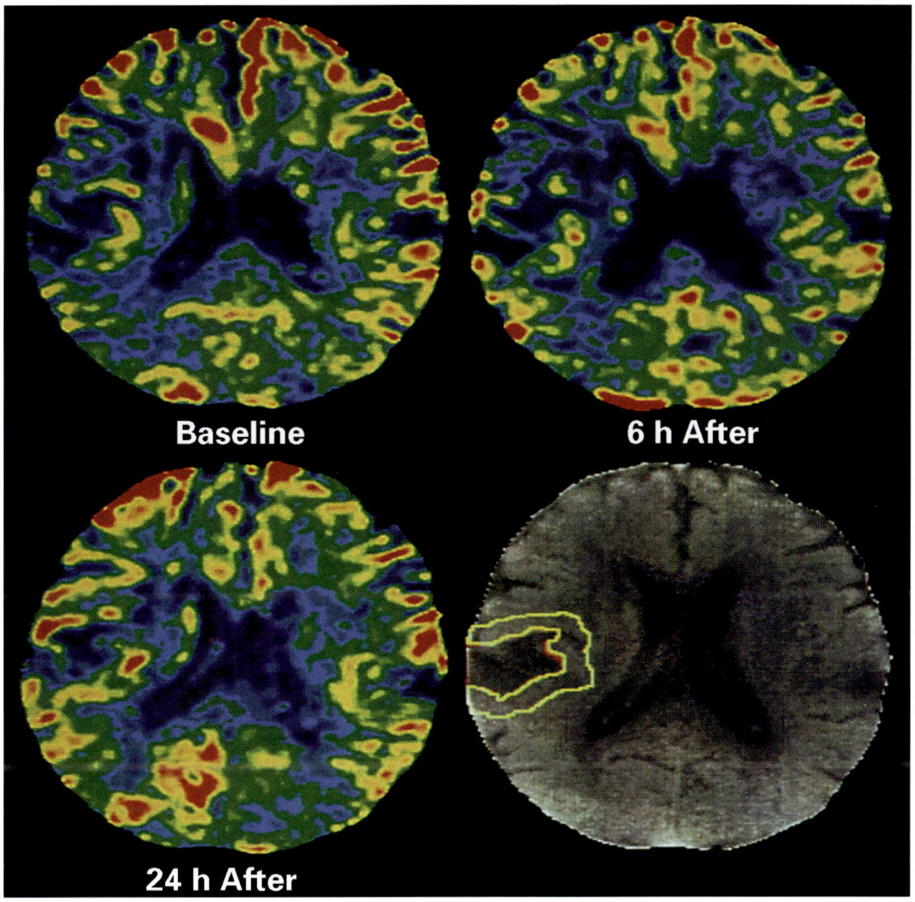

Fig. 5. Brain Xe CT scans at baseline (3 h), 6, and 12 h demonstrating hemispheric and penumbral rCBF of an ischemic stroke patient treated with argatroban.

23.7% in the placebo control group. Argatroban given later than 48 h after onset of symptoms produced a difference of 16% improvement over placebo (NS). Although levels of consciousness, subjective and psychological symptoms did not differ between the two groups, patients treated with argatroban showed statistically significant improvement compared with placebo for the ADL scale and the paralyzed leg scale (fig. 4). Brain CT scans showed that unchanged or decreased low-density areas were higher (but not significantly so) in the argatroban-treated group of patients. Adverse events reported in this study were low. Cerebral hemorrhage was detected in 1 of the 60 argatroban patients and in 2 of the 59 receiving placebo. All were minor and asymptomatic. After conclusion of this study, argatroban was approved for the treatment of thrombotic ischemic stroke when administered within 48 h of stroke symptom onset.

A further Japanese study involved patients with acute cerebral thrombosis, receiving argatroban [11]. This showed that by inhibiting thrombin activity, significant beneficial effects on regional cerebral blood flow occurred, postulated as due to protection of the penumbra. Furthermore, argatroban decreased FPA levels in these patients, indicating lower thrombin activity.

The effects of argatroban were further evaluated in a retrospective study of acute ischemic stroke patients. Subjects had xenon-CT regional cerebral blood flow (rCBF) scans at baseline and at prespecified time intervals following initiation of argatroban infusion therapy [12]. There was an increase in regional cerebral blood flow in the penumbra and in both hemispheres for both cortical and lacunar infarction when patients had scans performed at 3, 6 and 24 h following onset of stroke symptoms (fig. 5, 6).

These investigations suggest that argatroban therapy in acute ischemic stroke patients has the potential to reduce secondary microthrombi in the penumbra, improve regional cerebral blood flow, reduce ischemic lesions and ameliorate neurological deficits.

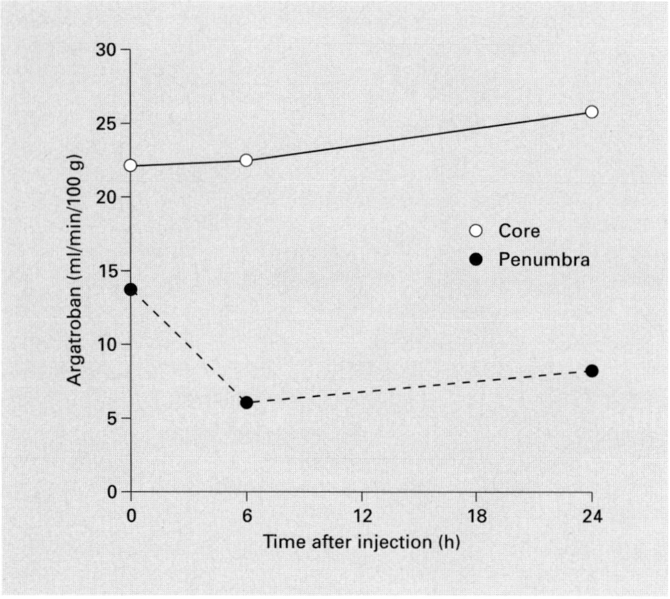

Fig. 6. Effect of argatroban on rCBF.

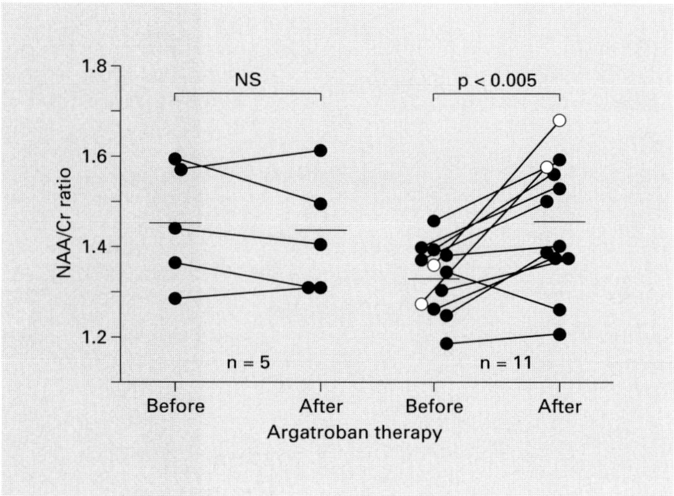

Fig. 7. NNA/Cr ratio in deep white matter measured by MRS.

Studies in the US investigating the benefit of argatroban in patients with heparin-induced thrombocytopenia with and without thrombosis syndrome (HIT, HITTS) found the direct thrombin inhibitor to reduce thrombosis events [13]. LaMonte et al. [14] reviewed the effects of argatroban therapy on neurologic complications in 1,005 HIT patients. Argatroban therapy, versus control, significantly reduced new stroke (1.8% versus 3.1%, $p = 0.032$) in HIT [LaMonte MP, Brown PM, Hursting M, in preparation]. Intracranial hemorrhage was rare with one occurring in an argatroban-treated patient after therapy had ceased.

A safety study of argatroban in acute ischemic stroke is being conducted in the USA and Canada. The Argatroban in Acute Ischemic Stroke (ARGIS-1) study is a randomized, double-blind, placebo-controlled trial testing safety and exploring the efficacy of argatroban in patients with acute ischemic stroke [15]. 65 centers participated in recruitment of 176 patients. Patients were randomly assigned to placebo versus one of two groups of argatroban treatment to produce two targeted aPTTs of 1.75 versus 2.25. Inclusion criteria allowed for ischemic stroke patients with NIH Stroke Scale (NIHSS) scores in the range of 5–22 to be enrolled up to 12 h after stroke symptom onset.

The primary outcome of the study is safety as determined by symptomatic intracerebral hemorrhage and other major bleeding events. Secondary outcomes included further safety analyses and exploration of the efficacy of argatroban using the NIHSS score, and the modified Rankin and Barthel Index scales. The study has completed enrollment and results become available in 2003.

Cerebrovascular diseases other than acute ischemic stroke may be the targets for treatment in the future. For example, a small pilot study from Japan assessed the use of argatroban in patients with chronic cerebrovascular disease [16]. A total of 17 patients, 15 with silent cerebral infarction and 2 with vascular dementia participated. Patients were monitored before and after therapy for changes in neuronal activity, measured by spectroscopy MRI scan changes in NAA/creatine ratio in the deep white matter of the brain. Changes in coagulation activation markers were also measured. The results indicated that in the 11 patients with advanced cerebrovascular disease, the mean NAA/Cr ratio increased significantly from baseline, suggesting an improvement in neuronal activity (fig. 7). Among patients with less pronounced cerebrovascular disease, these differences were not significant. Overall changes in coagulation activation markers were statistically significant for TAT, showing a fall from baseline of 11.0 to 5.9 (table 3).

Table 3. Changes in coagulation markers in patients with cerebrovascular diseases

	Total patients (n = 17)		Cerebrovascular disease			
			less (n = 5)		advanced (n = 12)	
	before	after	before	after	before	after
TAT, ng/ml	11	5.9[a]	11.3	8.22	11.0	4.93[b,c]
F1+2, nmol/l	1.40	0.97[b]	1.53	1.07[b]	1.35	0.94
D dimer, mg/dl	1.54	1.33	2.23	1.85	1.25	1.11
ATIII, %	93	102	97	103	92	101

[a] $p < 0.01$, [b] $p < 0.05$ versus before argatroban therapy.

Conclusions

There may be a role for thrombin inhibition in the treatment of cerebral ischemia. The mode of action of argatroban in cerebral thrombosis is explained as the inhibition of the local thrombin formed due to ischemic tissue damage. By preventing subsequent thrombus formation in the penumbral microcirculation it is hypothesized that improved blood flow to the peri-infarct penumbra would preserve neuronal cells at risk. In a clinical study of ischemic stroke in Japan, argatroban administered within 48 h of onset was found to safely and effectively reduce neurological deficit. A USA and Canadian study of argatroban's safety in acute ischemic stroke is ongoing. This multicenter, randomized, double-blind, placebo-controlled trial has a primary safety endpoint. Efficacy will be explored via a number of secondary outcomes.

References

1 Gubitz G, Counsell C, Sandercock P, Signrini D: Anticoagulants for acute ischaemic stroke (Cochrane Review). The Cochrane Library, Issue 2, 2001. Oxford: Update Software.
2 Collaborative group, CAST (Chinese Acute Stroke Trial): Randomized placebo-controlled trial of early aspirin use in 20,000 patients with acute ischemic stroke. Lancet 1997:349:1641–1649.
3 Chen ZM, Sandercock P, Pan HC, Collaborative group: The International Stroke Trial (IST): A randomized trial of aspirin, subcutaneous heparin, both, or neither among 19,435 patients with acute ischemic stroke. Lancet 1997;349:1569–1581.
4 Counsell C, Collins R, Liu LS, Xie JX, Warlaow C, Peto R: Indications for early aspirin use in acute ischemic stroke: A combined analysis of 40,000 randomized patients from the Chinese acute stroke trial and the international stroke trial. On behalf of the CAST and IST collaborative groups. Stroke 2000;316:1240–1249.
5 Counsell C, Sandercock P: Low-molecular-weight heparins or heparinoids versus standard unfractionated heparin for acute ischemic stroke (Cochrane Review). The Cochrane Library, Issue 2, 2001. Oxford: Update Software.
6 Uchiyama S, Yamazaki M, Hara Y, Iwata M: Alterations of platelet, coagulation and fibrinolysis markers in patients with acute ischemic stroke. Semin Thromb Haemost 1997;23:535–541.
7 Kario K, Komada K, Koide M, Matsuo T: Thrombin inhibition in the acute phase of ischaemic stroke using argatroban. Blood Coagul Fibrinolysis 1995;6:423–427.
8 Kawai K, Yuki S, Sugimoto J, Tamao Y: Effects of a thrombin inhibitor, argatroban, on ischemic brain damage in the rat distal middle cerebral artery occlusion model. J Pharmacol Exp Ther 1996;278:780–785.
9 Nakamura K: Thrombin-induced vasoconstriction in isolated cerebral arteries and the influence of a synthetic thrombin inhibitor. Thromb Res Suppl 1985;40:715–720.
10 Kobayashi S, Tazaki Y: Effect of the thrombin inhibitor argatroban in acute cerebral thrombosis. Semin Thromb Haemost 1997;23:531–534.
11 Tanaka Y, Kawabata S, Sin R, Takatuka K, Nisimura H, Yoshikawa N, Komato T: Therapeutic effect of argatroban (MD-805) antithrombin agent in the acute stage of cerebral thrombosis. J Clin Ther Med 1987;3:133–142.
12 Maruki T, Onada A, Matsuzaki M Narabayashi Y, Sawada M, Shimazu K: A specific thrombin inhibitor (argatroban) ameliorated cerebral blood flow in the patients with acute cerebral infarction. Keio J Med 2000;49(suppl 1):138–140.
13 Lewis BE, Wallis DE, Berkowitz DS, Matthai WH, Fareed J, Walenga JM, Bartholomew J, Sham R, Lerner RG, Zeigler ZR, Rustagi PK, Jong IK, Rifkin SD, Moran J, Hursting MJ, Kelton JG for the ARG-911 Study Investigators: Argatroban anticoagulant therapy in patients with heparin induced thrombocytopenia. Circulation 2001;103:1838–1843.
14 LaMonte M, Brown P, Berens KL: Reduction in stroke mortality in patients with heparin-induced thrombocytopenia after treatment with the direct thrombin inhibitor argatroban. Cerebrovasc Dis 2002;13(suppl 3):6.
15 LaMonte MP, Brown PM, Evans, DM: A randomized, placebo-controlled study to determine the safety and efficacy of argatroban injection in acute ischemic stroke (ARGIS I) (abstract). Cerebrovasc Dis 2002;13(suppl 3):6.
16 Kario K, Matsuo T, Shimada K: Department of Cardiology, Jichi Medical School, Department of IM. Hygo Prefectural Awaji Hospital, unpublished data.

Pathophysiology of Haemostasis and Thrombosis

Pathophysiol Haemost Thromb 2002;32(suppl 3):46–55
DOI: 10.1159/000069109

Argatroban in HIT Type II and Acute Coronary Syndrome

Bruce E. Lewis[a] Jeanine M. Walenga[b]

[a]Loyola University Medical Center, Maywood, Ill., Catholic Health Partners, Chicago, Ill.;
[b]Thoracic and Cardiovascular Surgery and Pathology, Loyola University Medical Center, Maywood, Ill., USA

Key Words

Argatroban · Thrombin inhibitor · Heparin antibody · Acute coronary syndrome

Abstract

Prior to initiation of the ARG-911 and ARG-915 clinical trials, there was no optimal replacement for heparin anticoagulation in patients with heparin-induced thrombocytopenia (HIT) type II. These prospective, historical controlled studies were designed to determine the usefulness of argatroban, a direct thrombin inhibitor (DTI) that is not immunogenic and does not interact with heparin antibody, in answering this clinical need. Clinical outcomes (37-day period) for 568 argatroban-treated and 193 control patients demonstrated significantly reduced risks of the primary efficacy composite endpoint (all-cause death, all-cause amputation, new thrombosis) and the secondary endpoints (death due to thrombosis, new thrombosis) with argatroban. Argatroban patients also experienced a more rapid recovery of platelet count. Bleeding events were similar among both groups. It was concluded that argatroban anticoagulation, compared with historical controls, improves clinical outcomes without increasing bleeding risk in patients having HIT with or without thrombosis. Argatroban has since been approved in the US for both prophylaxis and treatment of thrombosis in patients with HIT. Argatroban has been used in percutaneous coronary interventions in patients with and without HIT, for peripheral vascular procedures in both large and small vessels in HIT patients, and as an adjunct to thrombolytic therapy for the treatment of AMI. Treatment success rates and the same or less bleeding was demonstrated with argatroban compared to heparin controls. These pilot studies suggest that argatroban will provide reliable anticoagulation during interventional procedures. A consistent safety profile of argatroban has been demonstrated in all studies to date. The main attributes of argatroban are its rapid onset of action, fast reversibility of its anticoagulant effect, inhibition of clot-bound thrombin, easily monitored by the aPTT and ACT and no dosage adjustment in renal-impaired individuals. These properties make argatroban a predictable and useful anticoagulant for HIT and non-HIT patients.

Introduction

Argatroban is a small molecule direct thrombin inhibitor (DTI). This drug has been used in Japan for the management of thromboembolic disorders for over 10 years. Despite this and a large number of preclinical studies on the pharmacology of argatroban, clinical trials for argatroban in Europe and North America were only initiated in 1993.

KARGER

Fax +41 61 306 12 34
E-Mail karger@karger.ch
www.karger.com

1424–8832/02/0329–0046$18.50/0

Accessible online at:
www.karger.com/pht

Jeanine M. Walenga, PhD
Cardiovascular Institute, Loyola University Medical Center
2160 S. First Ave.
Maywood, IL 60153 (USA)
Tel. +1 708 327 2838, Fax +1 708 327 2849, E-Mail jwaleng@lumc.edu

Argatroban is of a class of drugs that differs in many respects from heparin, low molecular weight heparins and heparinoids [1–5]. Many of the characteristics common to thrombin inhibitors make argatroban beneficial for use as an anticoagulant in patients with heparin-induced thrombocytopenia (HIT). These attributes include no cross-reactivity with heparin antibody, no potentiation of HIT and absence of antibody formation (tables 1, 2).

The clinical utility of argatroban for the management of patients with HIT-associated thrombosis and in the setting of interventional cardiology will be reviewed.

Argatroban for HIT

Pathophysiology of HIT

HIT, type II, is a disease spectrum triggered by an immune response to heparin. HIT occurs in approximately 2% of all heparin-treated individuals. The currently accepted hypothesis of the pathophysiology of HIT is based on the development of an IgG antibody to the heparin-PF4 complex that recognizes the FcγRIIa receptor on platelets. Binding of the IgG complex causes platelet activation, aggregation and thrombin generation [6–10]. The antibody is not heparin specific, and has been shown to react with other highly sulfated materials [11, 12]. Other antibodies have been identified.

The IgG antibody binding to heparin-PF4 will also target PF4 bound to endothelial cell heparan sulfate [13–15]. Damaged endothelial cells can act as a starting point for the thrombotic event potentially through exposure of tissue factor that is enhanced by recruited monocytes and further tissue factor release from endothelial cells [13, 15–17]. The release of platelet microparticles rich in phospholipid further contributes to platelet aggregation, endothelial cell activation and thrombin generation [17, 18]. Evidence of important platelet-leukocyte activation suggests an interaction of hemostatic activation with an inflammatory process in HIT [19, 20].

Thus, the pathophysiological mechanism of HIT is characterized by platelet activation, thrombin generation, endothelial cell activation/injury and leukocyte activation [21].

Clinical Diagnosis of HIT

The diagnosis of HIT is often not easy or straightforward. Clinical criteria are most important, including platelet count and evidence of unexplained thrombosis. However, HIT can be present even with a normal platelet count [22–24]. Confirmation by specific laboratory tests is optimal but not always possible. Rechallenge with heparin after resolution of the thrombocytopenia to confirm the diagnosis of HIT is dangerous and should not be performed.

Table 1. Pharmacologic characteristics of argatroban

Selective, direct inhibitor of thrombin
Rapid onset of action
Rapidly reversed
Short half-life (~45 min i.v.)
Clearance through the liver
No need for dosage adjustment in renal-impaired patients
Inhibition of clot-bound thrombin
Not dependent on cofactors (e.g., AT, HCII)
Easily monitored by aPTT or ACT
Lesser bleeding risk than other DTIs
No cross-reactivity with heparin antibody
Absence of antibody formation that affect pharmacokinetics/activity

Table 2. Differences between the two DTIs argatroban and hirudin

Argatroban	Hirudin
Shorter half-life	Longer half-life
Anticoagulant response rapidly reversed	Anticoagulant response slowly reversed
No antibody formation to argatroban	Antibodies are generated that delay its elimination; antibodies are generated that decrease its anticoagulant activity
May have less bleeding side effects	May have more bleeding side effect
Metabolized in the liver	Cleared via the kidney
Requires dose adjustment in liver disease patients	Requires dose adjustment in renal disease patients
Effectively monitored by aPTT and ACT	Monitored by aPTT and ACT, but response times are different from argatroban

The most dramatic clinical expression of HIT is HIT antibody-driven thrombosis. HIT is probably a more common cause of thrombosis than has been appreciated. The majority of cases of HIT are found in medically and surgically treated adults but can also be observed from simple catheter line flush heparin [25], during pregnancy and in children. Postoperative coronary artery bypass patients have a high frequency of venous graft closure. Additionally, outpatients can develop thrombosis in the home setting.

Patients with clinically diagnosed HIT have a 35% probability of developing a clinically significant thrombosis during their hospitalization [22, 26, 27]. Patients with HIT associated thrombosis have a mortality rate of 25–30% and an amputation rate of 25%.

Thrombosis can occur anywhere throughout both the venous and the arterial circulation [22–24, 26]. Recent reports document a higher frequency of venous thrombosis than arterial thrombosis [26]. HIT-associated thrombosis is most commonly associated with deep vein thrombosis and pulmonary embolism, but unusual thromboses, including e.g., mesenteric ischemia, which is commonly overlooked, spinal artery thrombosis, visceral infarctions, cerebral infarction and myocardial infarction are not uncommon. Mesenteric infarction has been seen in 15% of patients, myocardial infarction in 20% and cerebral infarction in 10%.

Laboratory Diagnosis of HIT

There is no highly sensitive and specific laboratory test for HIT [28, 29]. The functional platelet aggregation assay using patient serum (antibody), heparin and donor platelets has several limitations including a high false-negative rate. The serotonin release assay (SRA) using washed donor platelets radiolabeled with ^{14}C-serotonin, patient serum and heparin has a higher sensitivity of 60–80%. Yet there can be patient samples negative by SRA that are positive by the aggregation test. Both the SRA and the aggregation assay are characterized by technical difficulties that require expert lab staff.

There are two Elisa tests for quantitating the antibody titer to the heparin-PF4 complex (Stago, Asnières, France and GTI, Brookfield, Wisc., USA). A minimum critical titer has not been identified that is associated with HIT thrombosis [28]. Heparin or low molecular weight (LMW) heparin treatment alone provokes antibody production that is not accompanied by thrombocytopenia or thrombosis [24, 29–32]. This common finding can lead to inappropriate treatment in patients who do not have HIT. On the other hand, patients clinically positive for HIT do not necessarily have positive Elisa antibody titers [28, 33]. Thus, although the Elisa is easy to perform, it does not provide results that are always clinically relevant.

As yet, there is no single assay that is ideal for diagnosing HIT. Each of the current assays for HIT contributes independent information. None can be used alone with complete confidence to identify a HIT-positive patient. Clinically positive patients could be missed by all assays, and antibody alone (Elisa positive) does not determine clinical HIT. Use of the Elisa method as a stand-alone test or as a rapid, preliminary screening test for HIT with confirmation by a follow-up SRA test should be discouraged. The combination of platelet aggregation, SRA and Elisa testing, with multiple samples, offers the best chance of identifying a positive HIT patient. Clinical observations remain of foremost importance in diagnosing HIT.

Clinical Management of HIT

The apparent paradox of a fall in platelet count with thrombotic rather than hemorrhagic complications is analogous to the syndrome of thrombotic thrombocytopenic purpura [23, 24]. HIT is clinically managed as an allergy to heparin. All heparin is immediately discontinued upon suspicion of the disease with a meticulous search for all sources of exogenous heparin. Due to the high probability of thrombosis, a vigorous search for venous and arterial thrombosis should be undertaken.

Unfortunately, early discontinuation of heparin does not significantly reduce the incidence of morbidity and mortality in patients with HIT [26]. It may be appropriate to use antithrombotic drugs as prophylaxis against thrombosis in this high-risk population. This practice has not been common, but this may relate more to the lack of appropriate prophylactic agents for this patient population than to the medical rationale. Today, use of a DTI can be recommended, initiated at a low level of anticoagulation until the thrombocytopenia resolves for patients with HIT antibody despite no other indication for anticoagulation. For patients with HIT-associated thrombosis, there is an immediate need to treat to avoid propagation of the clot or development of pulmonary embolism.

Other considerations for anticoagulation needs in the patient with HIT include patients with thrombosis for non-HIT-related events, such as myocardial infarction, unstable angina, heart valves and atrial fibrillation. Perhaps the greatest obstacle to overcome in the management of these patients is anticoagulation for coronary revascularization or cardiac surgery. For a short period, heparin has been used in patients who have negative antibody titers, albeit with some risk [23].

Traditional Therapies

The conventional anticoagulants aspirin and dextran are of limited value in the treatment of patients with HIT-associated thrombosis (table 3) [24, 34]. Coumadin derivatives require a loading period that leaves patients without anticoagulant protection for 48–72 h. Coumadin derivatives also inhibit protein C, potentially resulting in a prothrombotic state. Because of this, it is recommended that coumadin derivatives be initiated at low doses only when patients are out of the acute phase of HIT when platelet counts are on the rise [34].

Patients who have limb-threatening or life-threatening thrombosis can be treated with selective thrombolytic infusion, e.g., lower dose for postoperative patients and higher dose for non-postoperative patients [35, 36] until angiographic evidence of complete resolution of thrombus. Surgical thrombectomy remains a reasonable therapy in patients who have dire clinical circumstances and cannot afford the time required for selective thrombolytic infusions [23, 24]. However, the endothelial damage that occurs with thrombectomy, combined with the involvement of HIT antibody on endothelial cells, may explain the limited success with thrombectomy.

Anticoagulants other than heparin are necessary for proper treatment of patients with HIT (table 3). The early treatment alternatives have been less than optimal due to high bleeding risk, slow onset of action, long half-life, poor efficacy and lack of an antidote. These options have included the defibrinating agent ancrod (Arvin®; Knoll, Whippany, N.J., USA) [37, 38], and the heparinoid danaparoid (Orgaran®; Organon, Oss, The Netherlands) [39]. It has also been shown that heparin antibodies can cross-react with danaparoid [40].

LMW heparins appear to be less likely than heparin to cause HIT [31]; however, in vitro results unequivocally demonstrate that the heparin antibody recognizes LMW heparin producing platelet aggregation in a heparin-antibody-stimulated system [12, 40, 41]. Thus, LMW heparins should not be administered to patients with known heparin antibody.

Argatroban, a Direct Thrombin Inhibitor

An anticoagulant of a structure different from heparin, that has no ability to cross-react with the HIT antibody, would be the drug of choice for patients with HIT. The most promising class of drugs to date for treatment of patients with HIT are the DTIs. Argatroban (GlaxoSmithKline, Philadelphia, Pa., USA) is approved for the prophylaxis and treatment of HIT thrombosis in the USA. Among other beneficial characteristics, this drug does not cross-react with the heparin antibody as shown by in vitro data and successful treatment of HIT patients (table 1) [12, 19, 42].

Table 3. Anticoagulants for the treatment of thrombosis in patients with HIT

Drug	Status
Warfarin and dextran	limited efficacy; warfarin can be useful for long-term management after thrombin inhibitor treatment during acute phase
Selective thrombolytic infusion or surgical thrombectomy	useful for life-threatening thrombosis only
Ancrod (defibrinating agent)	difficult dosing regimen; slow onset of action; high bleeding risk; no antidote
Danaparoid (heparinoid)	monitoring not convenient; long half-life; high bleeding risk at high dose; no antidote; may cross-react with heparin antibody
Direct thrombin inhibitors	drug of choice
Factor Xa inhibitors	investigational
Anti-platelet drugs GPIIb/IIIa inhibitors ADP receptor inhibitors	investigational, alone or in combination with thrombin inhibitors

The ARG-911 was a multi-center study conducted to evaluate the safety and efficacy of argatroban in patients with HIT (table 4) [42]. Continuous intravenous argatroban was administered at 2 µg/kg/min continuous infusion for an average of 6 days (14 days maximum) to 304 HIT patients. Dosage was adjusted to maintain the activated partial thromboplastin time (aPTT) between 1.5–3.0 × baseline. Because there was no approved alternative agent for use as an active comparator when the studies were conducted, a historical control was used for comparison (n = 193).

Outcomes were assessed during and following therapy (37 days). The primary efficacy composite endpoint (new thrombosis, all-cause amputation, or all-cause death) was reduced significantly in argatroban-treated patients (n = 160) vs. controls (n = 147) with HIT (25.6 vs. 38.8%, p = 0.014). In patients with heparin-induced thrombocytopenia thrombosis syndrome (HITTS), the composite incidence in argatroban-treated patients was 43.8% (n = 144) vs. 56.5% (n = 46), p = 0.131. Significant between-group differences by time-to-event analysis of the com-

Table 4. Summary of the ARG-911 clinical trial of argatroban anticoagulation for patients with HIT and HITTS

	HIT	HITTS
Efficacy (p values in favor of argatroban over control)		
Composite endpoint[1]	0.014	0.131
Time to event	0.01	0.014
New thrombosis	<0.001	0.044
Death	<0.005	<0.001
Safety (p values in favor of argatroban over control)		
Major bleeding	0.078	0.077
Minor bleeding	NS	NS
Rapid rise in platelet count	0.001	
Therapeutic level achieved within 4–5 h		

[1] New thrombosis, all-cause amputation, all-cause death [42].

HIT was defined in this study as heparin induced thrombosis without new thrombosis after heparin initiation (latent HIT). HITTS was defined as heparin induced thrombosis complicated by thrombosis that occurred after heparin administration.

posite endpoint favored argatroban treatment in HIT (p = 0.01) and HITTS (p = 0.014) patients. Argatroban therapy, relative to controls, also significantly reduced any new thrombosis (p < 0.001 in HIT and p = 0.044 in HITTS patients) and death due to thrombosis (p < 0.005 in HIT and p < 0.001 in HITTS patients).

No difference was detected in the incidence of major bleeding (HIT: 3.1% for argatroban vs. 8.2% for control, p = 0.078; HITTS: 11.1% for argatroban vs. 2.2% for control, p = 0.077). Minor bleeding was similar in both arms (HIT: 40.0% for argatroban vs. 40.8% for control; HITTS: 41.7% for argatroban vs. 41.3% for control). Argatroban-treated patients achieved therapeutic aPTTs generally within 4–5 h of starting therapy. Compared to historic controls, argatroban-treated HIT and HITTS patients had a significantly more rapid rise in platelet count by day 3 (p = 0.0001).

This pivotal study showed that anticoagulation with argatroban significantly reduced the risk of thrombosis and thromboembolic complications of HIT/HITTS. This benefit was achieved without an increase in major bleeding. Based on the ARG-911 and a related clinical trial (ARG-915; n = 264) in which a total of 568 adult patients were treated with argatroban, the US FDA granted approval for the use of argatroban for both prophylaxis and treatment of thrombosis associated with HIT.

Argatroban in Comparison to Hirudin

Hirudin (lepirudin, Refludan®; Berlex, Wayne, N.J., USA) is another direct thrombin inhibitor. It is approved for treatment of HIT-associated thrombosis in the USA and Europe [43, 44], as DTIs hirudin and argatroban are similar. However, there are several pharmacologic characteristics that differ between the two drugs (table 2). Argatroban has a rapid onset of action, and it is rapidly dissociated from thrombin [2, 3, 45–48]. Argatroban has a shorter half-life than that of hirudin. The shorter half-life of argatroban seems to provide for easy clinical administration of the drug ('turn on-turn off') which seems to be reflected in a wider safety net (lesser bleeding) than that of hirudin. Argatroban is cleared through the liver; hirudin is cleared through the kidney. Hirudin is a protein and can generate antibodies that increase its anticoagulant activity by prolonging the half-life or antibodies that decrease its anticoagulant effect [49]. Argatroban does not induce antibody generation [50].

Argatroban with Coumadin Derivatives

For documented clinical thrombosis associated with HIT, patients should be treated with a DTI at therapeutic aPTT levels for 7–10 days. For patients with HIT and an underlying hypercoagulable state, mechanical prosthetic valves or atrial fibrillation, the ideal management strategy would be to initiate oral anticoagulation while maintaining a therapeutic level of anticoagulation with an intravenous DTI. To avoid skin necrosis, full anticoagulation with coumadin should not be achieved until platelet counts exceed 100,000/µl [34]. Once the INR for coumadin is stable in the therapeutic range, the intravenous DTI can be tapered off then discontinued. Low dose aspirin can be added to the regimen once coumadin is therapeutic.

Argatroban is easily monitored by the aPTT [1, 42, 46, 51, 52]. But one should be aware that the prothrombin time (PT)/International Normalized Ratio (INR) is also affected by DTIs [51, 53, 54]. Higher than expected INR values will be obtained for patients on a combination of DTI and coumadin but without the same relationship between INR and bleeding risk. A nomogram is available that can be used to help direct dosing. A practical recommendation is to co-administer the drugs until an INR of 4 is achieved. Argatroban can then be withdrawn and the INR reassessed. Another recommendation is to utilize the short half-life of argatroban. If clinically practical, blood for the INR assessment can be drawn after the argatroban infusion has been interrupted for 2 h.

Table 5. Summary of the pilot cardiology studies of argatroban

a Angioplasty: ARG-216/310/311[1]

	Argatroban	Heparin
Acute procedural success, %	94.5	94.0
Major bleeding, %	1.1	3.1

b Acute myocardial infarction: MINT; ARGAMI

	Argatroban		Heparin
	low dose[1]	high dose[2]	
Acute procedural success, patients presenting within 6 h, %	56.8	58.7	42.1
Acute procedural success, patients presenting within 3 h, %	–	57.1	20.0*
Composite endpoint at 30 days, %	32.0	25.5	37.5
Major bleeding, %	2.6	4.3	10.0

	Argatroban high dose[3]	Heparin
Acute procedural success, %	76	82
Major bleeding, %	19.5	20.0

Argatroban achieved adequate anticoagulation within 10 min of initiation.
* $p = 0.03$.
1 350 μg/kg bolus plus 25 μg/kg/min infusion.
2 100 μg/kg bolus plus 1 μg/kg/min infusion for 48–72 h.
3 100 μg/kg bolus plus 3 μg/kg/min infusion for 48–72 h.

Argatroban with Anti-Platelet Drugs

Despite the potent anticoagulant effect of DTIs as seen in the clinical trials, there remains an unacceptable level of thrombosis-related morbidity and mortality in HIT patients. The glycoprotein (GP) IIb/IIIa platelet receptor inhibitors (abciximab, eptifibatide and tirofiban) and the ADP platelet receptor inhibitor (clopidogrel) have been shown to inhibit the in vitro platelet activation and aggregation responses induced by HIT serum and heparin [15, 17, 19, 55]. This includes inhibition of the formation of thrombogenic platelet microparticles. The DTIs were not effective in suppressing this platelet activation.

Limited clinical experience suggests that a GPIIb/IIIa inhibitor as an adjunct to a DTI is effective at reducing thrombus that is resistant to DTI treatment alone [19]. A standard dose of a GPIIb/IIIa inhibitor can be administered with a reduced dose of the DTI. In a small group of HIT patients treated as such, there was no overt bleeding that required intervention and all patients exhibited clinical improvement or full recovery. Although promising, optimal dosing for this combination regimen has not yet been established.

Argatroban for Acute Coronary Syndrome

Percutaneous Coronary and Peripheral Intervention

Frequently, patients with HIT require coronary interventional procedures. The feasibility of using argatroban in this patient population was established several years ago [56–58]. Subsequently, two trials (ARG216 and ARG310/311) assessed the safety and efficacy of argatroban as anticoagulant therapy for percutaneous coronary interventional (PCI) procedures, including percutaneous transluminal coronary angioplasty, stent implantation or rotational atherectomy, on HIT patients (table 5) [59]. Patients (n = 91; 112 PCIs) were given 350 μg/kg bolus argatroban followed by a 25 μg/kg/min infusion. Efficacy of anticoagulation for argatroban-treated PCI HIT patients was measured by comparison to the Cleveland Clinic PCI angioplasty registry of heparin-treated non-HIT patients during the concordant time of patient enrollment. Safety of argatroban for PCIs was assessed by comparing the bleeding rate with argatroban to the heparin only arm of the EPILOG trial, which was also conducted during the same time period as patient enrollment in the argatroban PCI trials.

The 94.5% acute procedural success rate with argatroban compared favorably with the 94.0% procedural success rate with heparin in patients undergoing their initial PCI with argatroban. No unsatisfactory outcomes occurred during repeat PCIs with argatroban (n = 21). Only 1 patient experienced major peri-procedural bleeding. The safety of argatroban during PCI was at least equivalent to that of heparin during PCI (1.1% major bleed rate with argatroban vs 3.1% with heparin).

Adequate anticoagulation as measured by the activated clotting time (ACT) was achieved in 97.8% of argatroban-treated patients after the initial argatroban bolus. The target ACT for PCI of 300–450 s was achieved within 10 min of initiation of argatroban [57]. An ACT of >300 s was maintained throughout the interventional procedure in over 80% of the argatroban-treated patients. A repeat argatroban bolus of 150 μg/kg generally re-established a therapeutic ACT. An ACT of 200–250 s is recommended when argatroban is used in conjunction with a GPIIb/IIIa inhibitor.

Argatroban has also been used for PCI in a limited number of non-HIT patients [1, 60–62]. Three studies reported procedural success in all patients. Argatroban produced predictable anticoagulation and was generally safe and well tolerated.

Although the data are promising for the use of argatroban in PCI in HIT and non-HIT patients, the registry style control data collection used in some of these studies could have introduced observational bias due to the non-blinded nature of the study design. Argatroban is indicated as an anticoagulant in patients with or at risk for HIT undergoing PCI. (Source: Argatroban US prescribing information leaflet, April 2002.)

The use of argatroban for peripheral vascular procedures including carotid and renal arteries as well as cerebral vessels has not been formally studied; however, a number of case reports provide some information regarding the feasibility of argatroban in these situations [58, 63, 64]. Small vessel interventions on tibial and peroneal arteries or intracranial vessels can probably be safely performed using coronary argatroban dosing strategies (350 μg/kg bolus followed by 25 μg/kg/min infusion). Larger vessels such as iliac and renal arteries can probably be treated with lesser argatroban doses (250 μg/kg bolus followed by 10 μg/kg/min infusion).

Acute Myocardial Infarction

The investigation of argatroban as adjunct therapy to thrombolytics for patients with acute ST elevation myocardial infarction (MI) was performed in a three-arm clinical study, the MINT trial (Myocardial Infarction with Novastan and tPA) [65]. Patients, within 6 h of onset of symptoms for AMI, were randomized to low-dose argatroban (100 μg/kg bolus plus 1 μg/kg/min infusion for 48–72 h), high-dose (100 μg/kg bolus plus 3 μg/kg/min infusion for 48–72 h) argatroban or heparin as adjunct therapy to tPA (n = 125).

The primary efficacy outcome (rate of TIMI grade 3 flow at 90 min) was achieved in 42.1% of heparin, 56.8% of low-dose argatroban (p = 0.20 vs. heparin) and 58.7% of high-dose argatroban patients (p = 0.13 vs. heparin) (table 5). In patients presenting after 3 h, TIMI grade 3 flow was significantly more frequent in high-dose argatroban than heparin patients (57.1 vs. 20.0%; p = 0.03). Major bleeding was observed in 10.0% of heparin, and in 2.6 and 4.3% of low-dose and high-dose argatroban patients. The composite endpoint (death, recurrent MI, cardiogenic shock, congestive heart failure, revascularization, recurrent ischemia at 30 days) occurred in 37.5% of heparin, 32.0% of low-dose and 25.5% of high-dose argatroban patients (p = 0.23).

A second study was conducted which compared argatroban to heparin as adjunct therapy to alteplase (tPA) for the treatment of acute MI [66]. The ARGAMI (Argatroban in Acute Myocardial Infarction) study was an open dose-finding study (n = 35), followed by a placebo-controlled study with a double-dummy technique and a 2:1 (argatroban, n = 82:heparin, n = 45) randomization. An argatroban dose of 100 μg/kg bolus plus 3 μg/kg/min infusion for 72 h was selected for the randomized study. TIMI grade 2 or 3 flow after 90 min, not different between treatment groups, was obtained in 76% of the argatroban patients and in 82% of the heparin patients (not significant). Coronary angiography after 24 h and at 5–10 days showed similar low reocclusion rates in both groups. Bleeding complications, similar in both groups, were observed in 19.5% of the argatroban and in 20.0% of the heparin patients.

Summary

The introduction of direct thrombin inhibitor drugs, such as argatroban, has added a new dimension to the management of thrombosis (table 6). These drugs offer a unique substitute for anticoagulation in patients who are heparin compromised, a position we have not had prior to now. Based on clinical studies that have demonstrated the efficacy in patients with HIT, argatroban has been approved in the US for both prophylaxis and treatment of thrombosis in patients with HIT.

Table 6. Clinical uses of argatroban

Approved	
Prophylaxis against thrombosis in patients with heparin-induced thrombocytopenia	
Treatment of thrombosis in patients with heparin-induced thrombocytopenia	
Anticoagulation for patients with heparin-induced thrombocytopenia undergoing percutaneous coronary interventions	
Under investigation	
Interventional cardiology procedures	
	Angioplasty
	Stent implants
	Adjunct to thombolysis
Peripheral vascular procedures	
Cerebral vascular procedures	
Treatment of thrombotic stroke	
Other thrombotic disorders	
Hemodialysis	

The use of DTIs in acute coronary syndrome represents a new application of this class of drugs. Pooled data from the OASIS, TIMI and GUSTO clinical studies showed a significant reduction in cardiac events using hirudin compared to heparin. But unfortunately, it also showed a significant increase in bleeding. Treatment with the shorter-acting hirudin derivative, hirulog, was shown to be associated with both a lower incidence of ischemia and unstable angina and a decreased bleeding rate compared to heparin. Data from the CACHET trial showed a decrease in combined endpoints using DTIs during coronary intervention.

Limited studies suggest that argatroban will provide reliable anticoagulation during PCI and during peripheral vascular interventions in both large and small vessels in HIT patients. In patients with and without HIT procedural success rates similar to that of heparin were demonstrated. Argatroban has also been used in HIT patients with unstable angina and for the treatment of AMI as an adjunct to thrombolysis. Similar clinical outcomes to heparin-treated patients and no significant differences for major hemorrhage were observed with argatroban.

The main attributes of argatroban are its rapid onset of action, the fast reversibility of its anticoagulant effect, inhibition of clot-bound thrombin and no need for dosage adjustment in patients with renal impairment (tables 1, 2). Argatroban is easily monitored by the aPTT for low doses and the ACT for high doses. These properties make argatroban a predictable, safe, easy to dose anticoagulant. Argatroban will continue to be studied as an antithrombotic agent in additional clinical settings such as ischemic and thrombotic stroke and as an adjunct anticoagulant for various indications.

References

1 Jeske W, Walenga JM, Lewis BE, Fareed J: Pharmacology of argatroban. Exp Opin Invest Drugs 1999;8:625–654.
2 Hursting MJ, Alford KL, Becker JC, Brooks RL, Joffrion JL, Knappenberger GD, Kogan PW, Kogan TP, McKinney AA, Schwarz RP: Novastan (brand of argatroban): A small-molecule, direct thrombin inhibitor. Semin Thromb Hemost 1997;23:503–516.
3 Bush LR: Argatroban, a selective, potent thrombin inhibitor. Cardiovasc Drug Rev 1991;9:247–263.
4 Hijikata-Okunomiya A, Okamoto S: A strategy for a rational approach to designing synthetic selective inhibitors. Semin Thromb Hemost 1992;18:135–149.
5 Berry CN, Girard D, Lochot S, Lecoffre C: Antithrombotic actions of argatroban in rat models of venous, mixed and arterial thrombosis, and its effects on the tail transection bleeding time. Br J Pharm 1994;113:1209–1214.
6 Amiral J, Bridey F, Wolf M, Boyer-Neumann C, Fressinaud E, Vissac AM, Peynaud-Debayle E, Dreyfus M, Meyer D: Antibodies to macromolecular platelet factor 4-heparin complexes in heparin-induced thrombocytopenia: A study of 44 cases. Thromb Haemost 1995;73:21–28.
7 Greinacher A, Pötzsch B, Amiral J, Cummel V, Eichner A, Mueller-Eckhardt C: Heparin-associated thrombocytopenia: Isolation of the antibody and characterization of a multi-molecular PF-4 heparin complex as the major antigen. Thromb Haemost 1994;71:247–251.
8 Kelton, JG, Smith JW, Warkentin TE, Hayward CPM, Denomme GA, Horsewood P: Immunoglobulin G from patients with heparin-induced thrombocytopenia binds to a complex of heparin and platelet factor 4. Blood 1994;83:3232–3239.
9 Brandt JT, Isenhart CE, Osborne JM, Ahmed A, Anderson CL: On the role of platelet FcRIIA phenotype in heparin-induced thrombocytopenia. Thromb Haemost 1995;74:1564–1572.
10 Aster RH: Heparin-induced thrombocytopenia and thrombosis. N Engl J Med 1995;332:1374–1376.
11 Greinacher A, Michels I, Liebenhoff U, Presek P, Mueller-Eckhardt C: Heparin-associated thrombocytopenia: Immune complexes are attached to the platelet membrane by the negative charge of highly sulfated oligosaccharides. Br J Haematol 1993;84:711–716.
12 Walenga JM, Koza MJ, Lewis BE, Pifarré R: Relative heparin induced thrombocytopenic potential of low molecular weight heparins and new antithrombotic agents. Clin Appl Thromb Hemost 1996;2(suppl 1):S21–S27.
13 Cines DB, Tomaski A, Tannenbaum S: Immune endothelial-cell injury in heparin associated thrombocytopenia. N Engl J Med 1987; 316:581–589.
14 Visentin GP, Ford SE, Scott JP, Aster RH: Antibodies from patients with heparin-induced thrombocytopenia/thrombosis are specific for platelet factor 4 complexed with heparin or bound to endothelial cells. J Clin Invest 1995; 93:81–88.

15 Herbert J-M, Savi P, Jeske WP, Walenga JM: Effect of SR121566A, a potent GPIIb/IIIa antagonist, on the HIT serum/heparin-induced platelet mediated activation of human endothelial cells. Thromb Haemost 1998;80:326–331.
16 Pouplard C, Iochmann S, Renard B, Herault O, Colombat P, Amiral J, Gruel Y: Induction of monocyte tissue factor expression by antibodies to heparin-platelet factor 4 complexes developed in heparin-induced thrombocytopenia. Blood 2001;97:3300–3302.
17 Jeske WP, Walenga JM, Szatkowski E, Ero M, Herbert JM, Bakhos M: Effect of glycoprotein IIb/IIIa antagonists on the HIT serum induced activation of platelets. Thromb Res 1997;88: 271–281.
18 Warkentin TE, Hayward CPM, Boshkov CK, Santos AV, Sheppard JI, Bode AP, Kelton JG: Sera from patients with heparin-induced thrombocytopenia generate platelet-derived microparticles with procoagulant activity: An explanation for the thrombotic complications of heparin-induced thrombocytopenia. Blood 1994;84:3691–3699.
19 Walenga JM, Lewis BE, Jeske WP, Leya F, Wallis DE, Bakhos M, Fareed, J: Combined thrombin and platelet inhibition treatment for HIT patients. Hämostaseologie 1999;19:128–133.
20 Jeske WP, Vasaiwala S, Schlenker R, Wallis E, Walenga JM: Leukocyte activation in heparin-induced thrombocytopenia (abstract). Blood 2000;96:29b.
21 Walenga JM, Jeske WP, Messmore HL: Mechanisms of venous and arterial thrombosis in heparin-induced thrombocytopenia. J Thromb Thrombolysis 2000;10(suppl 1):S13–S20.
22 Lewis BE, Walenga JM, Wallis DE: Anticoagulation with Novastan (argatroban) in patients with heparin-induced thrombocytopenia and heparin-induced thrombocytopenia and thrombosis syndrome. Semin Thromb Hemost 1997;23:197–202.
23 Messmore HL, Upadhyay G, Farid S, Parachuri R, Wehrmacher W, Godwin J: Heparin-induced thrombocytopenia and thrombosis in cardiovascular surgery; in Pifarré R (ed): New Anticoagulants for the Cardiovascular Patient. Philadelphia, Hanley & Belfus, 1993, pp 83–94.
24 Walenga JM, Lewis BE, Hoppensteadt DA, Fareed J, Bakhos M: Management of heparin-induced thrombocytopenia and heparin-induced thrombocytopenia and thrombosis syndrome. Clin Appl ThrombHemost 1997;3 (suppl 1):S53–S63.
25 Moberg P, Geary V, Sheikh M: Heparin-induced thrombocytopenia: A possible complication of heparin-coated pulmonary artery catheters. J Cardiothorac Vasc Anesth 1990;4:266.
26 Wallis DE, Workman DL, Lewis BE, Steen L, Pifarré R, Moran JF: Failure of early heparin cessation as treatment for heparin-induced thrombocytopenia. Am J Med 1999;106:629–635.
27 Warkentin T, Kelton J: A 14-year study of heparin-induced thrombocytopenia. Am J Med 1996;101:502–507.
28 Walenga JM, Jeske WP, Wood JJ, Ahmad S, Lewis BE, Bakhos M: Laboratory tests for heparin-induced thrombocytopenia: A multicenter study. Semin Hematol 1999;36(suppl 1):22–28.
29 Walenga JM, Jeske WP, Fasanella AR, Wood JJ, Bakhos M: Laboratory tests for the diagnosis of heparin-induced thrombocytopenia. Semin Thromb Hemostas 1999;25(suppl 1): 43–49.
30 Lindhoff-Last E, Eichler P, Stein M, Plagemann J, Gerdsen F, Wagner R, Ehrly AM, Bauersachs R: A prospective study on the incidence and clinical relevance of heparin-induced antibodies in patients after vascular surgery. Thromb Res 2000;97:387–393.
31 Warkentin TE, Levine MN, Hirsh J, Horsewood P, Roberts RS, Gent M, Kelton JG: Heparin-induced thrombocytopenia in patients treated with low-molecular-weight heparin or unfractionated heparin. N Engl J Med 1995; 332:1330–1335.
32 Bauer TL, Arepally G, Konkle BA, Mestichelli B, Shapiro SS, Cines DB, Poncz M, McNulty S, Amiral J, Hauck WW, Edie RN, Mannion JD: Prevalence of heparin-associated antibodies without thrombosis in patients undergoing cardiopulmonary bypass surgery. Circulation 1997;95:1242–1246.
33 Prechel M, Bano A, Drenth AF, Messmore HL, Walenga JM: Assay selection and interpretation for laboratory testing of heparin-induced thrombocytopenia: Diagnostic implications. Blood 2001;98:36a.
34 Wallis DE, Quintos R, Wehrmacher W, Messmore H: Safety of warfarin anticoagulation in patients with heparin-induced thrombocytopenia. Chest 1999;116:1333–1338.
35 Rao RC, Lewis BE, Johnson SA: Thrombolytic experience for treatment of thrombosis in patients with post-operative heparin-induced thrombocytopenia (abstract). Blood 1995;86 (suppl 1):551a.
36 Cohen JI, Cooper MR, Greenberg CS: Streptokinase therapy of pulmonary emboli with heparin-associated thrombocytopenia. Arch Intern Med 1985;135:1725–1726.
37 Cole CW, Bormanis J: Ancrod: A practical alternative to heparin. J Vasc Surg 1988;8:59–63.
38 Lewis BE, Leya FS, Wallis D, Grassman E: Failure of ancrod in the treatment of heparin-induced arterial thrombosis. Can J Cardiol 1994;10:559–561.
39 Magnani HN: Heparin-induced thrombocytopenia (HIT): An overview of 230 patients treated with Orgaran (Org 10172). Thromb Haemost 1993;70:554–561.
40 Haas S, Walenga JM, Jeske WP, Fareed J: Heparin-induced thrombocytopenia: Clinical considerations of alternative anticoagulation with various glycosaminoglycans and thrombin inhibitors. Clin Appl Thromb Hemost 1999;5: 52–59.
41 Greinacher A, Feigl M, Mueller-Eckhardt C: Cross-reactivity studies between sera of patients with heparin associated thrombocytopenia and a new low molecular weight heparin, reviparin. Thromb Haemost 1994;72:644–645.
42 Lewis BE, Wallis DE, Berkowitz SD, Matthai WH, Fareed J, Walenga JM, Bartholomew J, Sham R, Lerner RG, Zeigler ZR, Rustagi PK, Jang IK, Rifkin SD, Moran J, Hursting MJ, Kelton JG, for the ARG-911 Study Investigators: Argatroban anticoagulant therapy in patients with heparin-induced thrombocytopenia. Circulation 2001;103:1838–1843.
43 Greinacher A, Volpel H, Janssens U, Hach-Wunderle V, Kemkes-Matthes B, Eichler P, Mueller-Velten HG, Pötzsch B, for the HIT Investigators Group: Recombinant hirudin (lepirudin) provides safe and effective anti-coagulation in patients with heparin-induced thrombocytopenia: A prospective study. Circulation 1999;99:73–80.
44 Greinacher A, Janssens U, Berg G, Bock M, Kwasny H, Kemkes-Matthes B, Eichler P, Volpel H, Pötzsch B, Luz M, for the Heparin-Associated Thrombocytopenia Study (HAT) investigators. Lepirudin (recombinant hirudin) for parenteral anticoagulation in patients with heparin-induced thrombocytopenia. Circulation 1999;100:587–593.
45 Izawa O, Katsuki M, Komatsu T, Iida S: Pharmacokinetics studies of argatroban (MD-805) in human – Concentrations of argatroban and its metabolites in plasma, urine and feces during and after drip intravenous infusion (in Japanese). Jpn Pharmacol Ther 1986;14 (suppl 5):251–263.
46 Bergougnan L, Moore N, Brohier S: Pharmacodynamic and pharmacokinetic profile of argatroban (1 mg/ml alcohol solution) in healthy man. J Clin Pharmacol 1998;38:878.
47 Swan SK, Hursting MJ: The pharmacokinetics and pharmacodynamics of argatroban: Effects of age, gender, and hepatic or renal dysfunction. Pharmacotherapy 2000;20:318–329.
48 Swan SK, St Peter JV, Lambrecht LJ, Hursting MJ: Comparison of anticoagulant effects and safety of argatroban and heparin in healthy subjects. Pharmacotherapy 2000;20:756–770.
49 Eichler P, Friesen H-J, Lubenow N, Jaeger B, Greinacher A: Anti-hirudin antibodies in patients with heparin-induced thrombocytopenia treated with lepirudin: Incidence, effects on aPTT, and clinical relevance. Blood 2000;96: 2373–2378.
50 Walenga JM, Ahmad S, Hoppensteadt D, Iqbal O, Hursting MJ, Lewis BE: Argatroban therapy does not generate antibodies that alter its anticoagulant activity in patients with heparin-induced thrombocytopenia. Thromb Res 2002; 105:401–405.
51 Walenga JM, Fasanella AR, Iqbal O, Hoppensteadt DA, Ahmad S, Wallis DE, Bakhos M: Coagulation laboratory testing in patients treated with argatroban. Semin Thromb Hemost 1999;25(suppl 1):61–66.

52 Ahmad S, Ahsan A, Iqbal O, Hoppensteadt DA, Lewis BE, Walenga JM, Fareed J: Pharmacokinetics and pharmacodynamics of argatroban as studied by HPLC and functional methods: Implications in the monitoring and dosage-optimizations in cardiovascular patients. Clin Appl Thromb Hemost 1998;4:243–249.
53 Sheth SB, DiCicco RA, Hursting MJ, Montague T, Jorkasky DK: Interpreting the international normalized ratio (INR) in individuals receiving argatroban and warfarin. Thromb Haemost 2001;85:435–440.
54 Hursting MJ, Zehnder JL, Joffrion JL, Becker JC, Knappenberger GD, Schwarz RP: The interventional normalization ratio during concurrent warfarin and argatroban anticoagulation differential contributions of each agent and effects of the choice of the thromboplastin used. Clin Chem 1999;45:409–412.
55 Haas S, Walenga JM, Jeske WP, Fareed J: Heparin-induced thrombocytopenia: The role of platelet activation and therapeutic implications. Semin Thromb Hemost 1999;25 (suppl 1):67–75.
56 Lewis BE, Ferguson JJ, Grassman ED, Fareed J, Walenga JM, Joffrion JL, Wrona L, Johnson SA, Schwarz RP, McKiernan T: Successful coronary interventions performed with argatroban anticoagulation in patients with heparin-induced thrombocytopenia and thrombosis syndrome. J Invas Cardiol 1996;8:410–417.
57 Lewis BE, Iqbal O, Hoppenstaedt D, Ahsan A, Ahmad S, Messmore HL, Schwarz RP, Walenga JM: Clinical pharmacokinetic and pharmacodynamic studies on argatroban to optimize the anticoagulant dosage in interventional cardiovascular procedures (abstract). Thromb Haemost 1997(suppl);492.
58 Lewis BE, Rangel Y, Fareed J: The first report of successful carotid stent implant using argatroban anticoagulation in a patient with heparin-induced thrombocytopenia and thrombosis syndrome: A case report. Angiology 1998;49: 61–67.
59 Lewis BE, Matthai WH Jr, Cohen M, Moses JW, Hursting MJ, Leya F, ARG-216/310/311 Study Investigators: Argatroban anticoagulation during percutaneous coronary intervention in patients with heparin-induced thrombocytopenia. Catheter Cardiovasc Interv 2002; 57:177–184.
60 Itoh T, Nonogi H, Miyazaki S, Itoli A, Daikoko S: Local delivery of argatroban using drug delivery device 'dispatch' in the prevention of restenosis following coronary angioplasty trial (40-CAT): Result of the prospective randomized pilot study. Circulation 1997;96:3635.
61 Kobayashi H, Suzuki S, Sakamoto S, Matsuo T: Argatroban, a direct thrombin inhibitor versus heparin during and after percutaneous transluminal coronary angioplasty (PTCA) (abstract). Thromb Haemost 1997(suppl);494.
62 Herrman JP, Suryapranata H, den Heijer P, Gabriel L, Kutryk MJB, Serruys PW: Argatroban during percutaneous transluminal coronary angioplasty: Results of a dose-verification study. J. Thromb Thrombolysis 1996;3:367–375.
63 Lewis BE, Grassman ED, Wrona L, Rangel Y: Novastan anticoagulation during renal stent implant in a patient with heparin-induced thrombocytopenia. Blood Coagul Fibrinolysis 1997;8:54–58.
64 Kobayashi S, Tazaki Y: Effect of the thrombin inhibitor argatroban in acute cerebral thrombosis. Semin Thromb Hemost 1997;23:531–534.
65 Jang IK, Brown DF, Giugliano RP, Anderson HV, Losordo D, Nicolau JC, Dutra OP, Bazzino O, Viamonte VM, Norbady R, Liprandi AS, Massey TJ, Dinsmore R, Schwarz RP: A multicenter, randomized study of argatroban versus heparin as adjunct to tPA in acute MI: MI with novastan and tPA study (MINT). J Am Coll Cardiol 1999;33:1879–1885.
66 Vermeer F, Vahanian A, Fels PW, Besse P, Muller E, van deWerf F, Fitzgerald D, Darius H, Puel J, Garrigou D, Simoons ML: Argatroban and alteplase in patients with acute myocardial infarction: The ARGAMI study. J Thromb Thrombolysis 2000;10:233–240.

Pathophysiology
of Haemostasis
and Thrombosis

Pathophysiol Haemost Thromb 2002;32(suppl 3):56–65
DOI: 10.1159/000069110

Practical Issues in the Development of Argatroban: A Perspective

Jawed Fareed Debra Hoppensteadt Omer Iqbal Mehmut Tobu
Bruce E. Lewis

Departments of Pathology and Pharmacology, Loyola University Medical Center, Maywood, Ill., USA

Key Words
Antithrombin · Anticoagulant · Thrombosis · Reversible inhibitor

Abstract
Argatroban was the very first antithrombin agent that was approved for clinical use. It represents a synthetic arginomimetic drug with multiple pharmacologic properties. Unlike other antithrombin drugs, argatroban is a reversible antithrombin agent. Furthermore, it modulates endothelial cell function and downregulates various inflammatory and thrombotic cytokines. Argatroban is an effective anticoagulant agent, which at equivalent anticoagulant levels (activated clotting time; ACT) produces a stronger anticoagulant effect in comparison to heparins and hirudins. At a comparable ACT (300 s), argatroban produces much stronger inhibition of thrombin generation as measured by $F_{1.2}$ and thrombin-antithrombin complex generation. Argatroban does not generate any neutralizing or non-neutralizing antibodies and, therefore, it does not require any dosage adjustment during the course of therapy as other thrombin inhibitors require. The pharmacological profile of argatroban is unique as this antithrombin drug not only inhibits thrombogenesis but also modulates cellular functions. Because of its broad spectral actions, argatroban will have more expanded indications.

Introduction and Overview

The central role of thrombin in coagulation and platelet activation is now well established. Thus, this enzyme provides an important target to control thrombogenesis [1–3]. Thrombin inhibitors such as recombinant hirudin, hirulog, and argatroban are currently being developed for various clinical indications [4–12]. These drugs produce a direct anticoagulant response by targeting thrombin and plasmatic and cellular sites dependent on thrombin. In addition to amplifying the coagulation cascade by activating factors V and VIII, mediating stabilization of fibrin by activating factor XIII and activating platelets, thrombin exerts several regulatory activities to maintain hemostatic balance. It is capable of activating protein C, which is an anticoagulant and profibrinolytic enzyme [13]. Furthermore, thrombin is a potent stimulator of secretion of tissue-type plasminogen activator from endothelial cells [13–15]. Although plasminogen is activated to

KARGER
Fax +41 61 306 12 34
E-Mail karger@karger.ch
www.karger.com

© 2002 S. Karger AG, Basel
1424–8832/02/0329–0056$18.50/0

Accessible online at:
www.karger.com/pht

Dr. Jawed Fareed, Professor of Pathology and Pharmacology
Director of Hemostasis Research Laboratories
Loyola University Chicago, Stritch School of Medicine
2160 South First Avenue, Maywood, IL 60153 (USA)
Tel. +1 708 216 3262, Fax +1 708 216 6660, E-Mail jfareed@lumc.edu

plasmin directly by endogenous enzymes such as urokinase-type plasminogen activator and tissue-type plasminogen activator [16, 17], other enzymes such as kallikrein [18], factor XIIa [19], activated protein C [13, 14] and carboxypeptidase U (thrombin-activatable fibrinolytic inhibitor) also promote the activation of plasminogen. Some of the synthetic thrombin inhibitors are capable of producing inhibition of these enzymes [20–22]. Thus, both physiologic and pharmacologic fibrinolysis can be compromised. Thrombin inhibitors, therefore, exert a complex effect on the coagulation network and need to be carefully evaluated in clinical trials.

In the absence of heparin, thrombin is marginally neutralized by endogenous inhibitors such as heparin cofactor II and antithrombin, and because of their mass, these inhibitors are not capable of effectively neutralizing clot-bound thrombin. On the other hand, the lower mass of thrombin inhibitors allows these agents to penetrate the thrombus and inhibit the thrombin contained within, to control further growth of the thrombus. Thus, smaller molecular weight thrombin inhibitors are capable of producing the inhibition of clot-bound thrombin and may be more effective than heparin. Direct thrombin inhibitors can be classified according to source (endogenous, analogues of natural substrates, recombinant and synthetic), structure and type of physiological interactions. Some of these agents are directed against the catalytic site of thrombin while others bind to the exosites of thrombin. In addition, some are reversible inhibitors while others are irreversible. A list of currently available site-directed thrombin inhibitors is given in table 1. These agents are also depicted in figure 1.

Among the natural thrombin inhibitors, hirudin is one of the most potent thrombin inhibitors, found in the saliva of the leech, *Hirudo medicinalis*. It is a single polypeptide chain of 65 amino acid residues, stabilized in a characteristic conformation by three disulfide bridges [23, 24]. Hirudin and its variants have been produced by recombinant technology. Point mutations to develop variant forms of hirudin have been used [25]. More recently, polyethylene glycol coupling of recombinant hirudin, to develop longer-lasting agents, has been accomplished [12]. Several experimental and clinical trials have shown that polyethylene glycol coupling of hirudin produces an increase in the efficacy of the drug. Various derivatives of hirudin

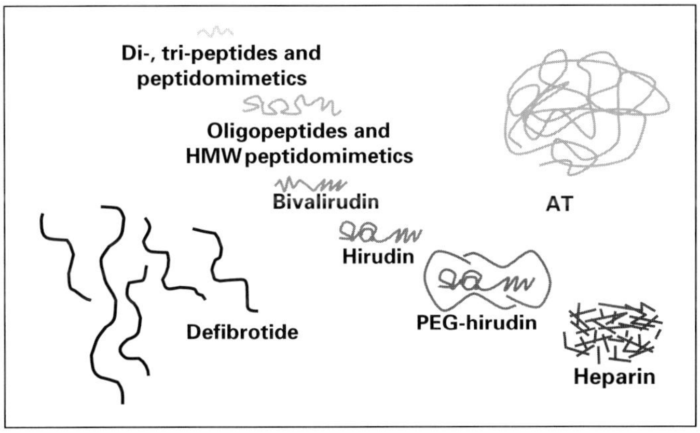

Fig. 1. A diagrammatic representation of various antithrombin drugs. As can be seen, the antithrombin agents represent a wide variety of chemical structures with functional and structural diversity.

Table 1. Developmental status of site-directed thrombin inhibitors

Agents	Chemical nature	Developmental status
Hirudin, PEG-hirudin and related variants	recombinant analogues of natural hirudin and their derivatives	various clinical phases of development; additional derivatives are being developed; one product is available in Europe and USA
Bivalirudin	synthetic bifunctional oligopeptides	phase II and III clinical studies completed; available in USA; additional studies are being carried out
Peptidomimetics	synthetic heterocyclic derivatives	phase II and III clinical development in the USA; one product available in USA, Canada and Japan; additional clinical development in USA and Europe
Peptides and their derivatives	peptide arginals and boronic acid peptide derivatives	phase II clinical development of various products
Aptamers and defibrotide	DNA- and RNA-derived oligonucleotides with thrombin-binding domains	preclinical stage; limited animal data available

are being aggressively developed for several clinical indications.

Coupling of peptides that mimic the carboxy terminal of hirudin to peptides that are specific for inhibition of the catalytic site of thrombin (D-Phe-Pro-Arg) has led to the development of a series of chimeric molecules termed hirulogs, in which the amino terminus consists of the catalytic site-directed peptides, while the carboxy terminus consists of the 12 terminal residues of hirudin. The two moieties are linked together by a bridge of glycine residues of variable length. Thus, hirulogs inhibit thrombin by binding to both its catalytic site and its anion-binding exosite, thus conferring specificity to these molecules for thrombin. One formulation, bivalirudin, has been developed aggressively for several cardiovascular indications [27]. However, its superiority over heparin has not been established.

Synthetic inhibitors of thrombin have long been used for the inhibition of thrombin. Of these inhibitors, the peptide derivatives mimicking the cleavage site in fibrinogen and peptidomimetics have provided therapeutic agents which are currently developed for various clinical indications. Of these, the most successful agent is an arginomimetic drug, argatroban, which represents the first thrombin inhibitor in clinical use. This reversible thrombin inhibitor is a direct inhibitor of thrombin and was synthesized by Okamoto et al. [26] in 1980. Japan is the first country where this thrombin inhibitor was approved for the treatment of peripheral occlusive vascular disease in the early 1990s. Subsequently, this drug was approved for acute cerebral thrombosis and for anticoagulation in thrombophilic patients requiring hemodialysis. In the year 2000, argatroban was approved in the US for the anticoagulant management of patients with heparin-induced thrombocytopenia [9, 27]. In early 2002, the FDA approved its usage in the anticoagulant management of HIT requiring percutaneous intervention (PCI) [10]. In addition to these approved indications, argatroban is now under clinical development for use in thrombotic and ischemic stroke.

Argatroban belongs to the peptidomimetic (arginomimetic) group of drugs with multiple pharmacologic properties. Unlike the other antithrombin drugs, such as hirudins and bivalirudin, argatroban is a fast reversible antithrombin agent and therefore exhibits a considerably different pharmacological profile. Although argatroban is considered to be a member of the antithrombin drug family, its mechanisms of action include several other steps that are not fully explored at this time. These include the inhibition of non-thrombin serine proteases, direct effect on endothelial cells and vasculature and downregulation of various inflammatory and thrombotic cytokines.

Because of its relatively lower molecular weight, argatroban is capable of passing through endovascular and cellular barriers and could possibly, therefore, be more effective than heparins and hirudins in the antithrombotic management of microvascular disorders. Argatroban is an effective anticoagulant agent, which at equivalent anticoagulant levels (activated clotting time; ACT) produces a stronger inhibition of thrombin generation in comparison to heparins and hirudins. At an ACT of 300 s, argatroban produces much stronger inhibition of thrombin generation as measured by prothrombin fragment $F_{1.2}$ and thrombin-antithrombin complex generation compared to heparin. Argatroban does not generate any neutralizing or non-neutralizing antibodies and, therefore, unlike lepirudin does not require any dosage adjustment due to the effects of drug-antibody interaction. It also does not produce individual variations between patients and has predictable clinical effects.

Beside the inhibition of thrombogenesis, argatroban also produces facilitation of blood flow, inhibition of platelet activation and endothelial cell stimulation. Not all of these mechanisms are related to the inhibition of thrombin. Unlike the tight binding thrombin inhibitors, argatroban does not compromise thrombin regulatory processes. Some of these regulatory actions are given below:

- inhibition of factor XIIIa;
- antagonism of protein C activation;
- activation of thrombin-activatable fibrinolytic inhibitor;
- inhibition of thrombin-mediated hemostatic effects of platelets;
- inhibition of the vasomodulatory effects of thrombin, and
- modulation of inflammatory cytokines.

Developmental Issues

Despite several advantages, further preclinical investigations are needed to validate the application of argatroban in additional clinical indications. The following represents a compilation of some of the potential questions related to the development of argatroban as an antithrombin drug. The responses to each of these questions are based on the available information.

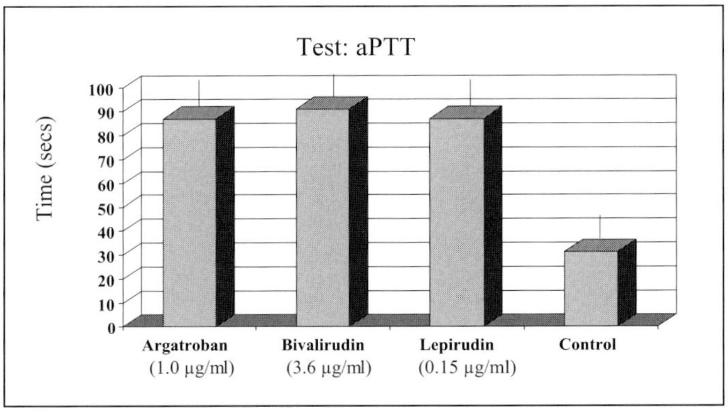

Fig. 2. Therapeutic anticoagulant effects of various anti-thrombin agents (aPTT 80–90 s). As can be seen, each drug produces the same prolongation of the aPTT at different concentrations. The mechanisms of their interactions are also different.

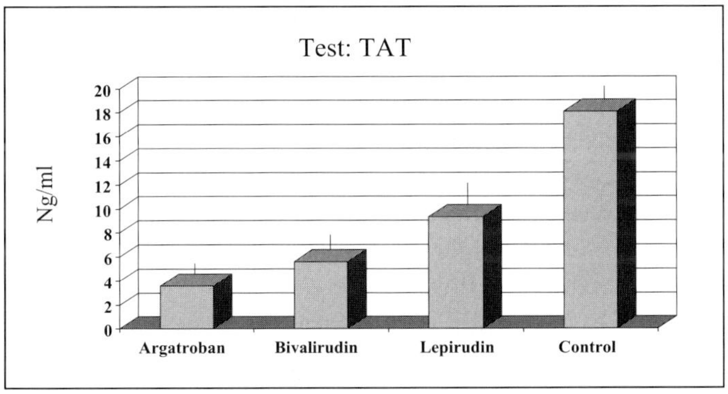

Fig. 3. Differential inhibition of thrombin-antithrombin complex by various thrombin inhibitors at equivalent therapeutic anticoagulant states (aPTT 80–90 s). As can be seen, each drug exhibits a specific inhibitory action. The order of potency is argatroban > bivalirudin > lepirudin.

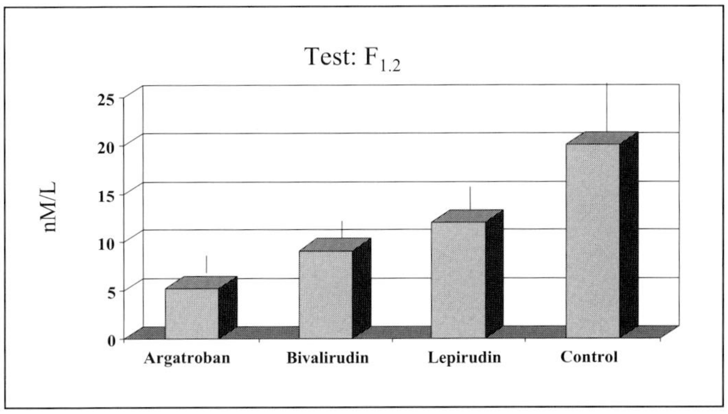

Fig. 4. Differential inhibition of $F_{1.2}$ generation by various thrombin inhibitors at equivalent therapeutic anticoagulant levels (aPTT 80–90 s). As can be seen, each drug exhibits a specific inhibitory action. The order of potency is argatroban > bivalirudin > lepirudin.

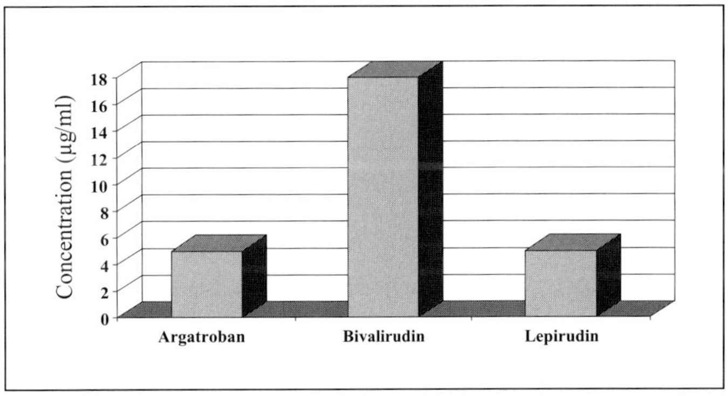

Fig. 5. Concentrations of thrombin inhibitors required to give ACT of 300 s. Differential ACT prolongation by various thrombin inhibitors in human whole blood. Relatively higher concentrations are required to increase the prolongation of the ACT (to levels used in interventional procedures) compared to the aPTT.

How Different Is Argatroban from Other Approved Antithrombin Agents?

While thrombin inhibitors are usually evaluated in terms of their relative ability to inhibit the clotting or amidolytic actions of thrombin, their ability to inhibit thrombogenesis does not correlate with their antithrombin potency. Argatroban is a fast reversible inhibitor of thrombin. In contrast, hirudin and PEG-hirudin are slowly reversible inhibitors. Bivalirudin is also different from argatroban in terms of its mechanism of action as it is a bivalent inhibitor. As shown in figure 2, the relative concentrations needed to produce comparable prolongation of activated partial thromboplastin time (aPTT) to achieve therapeutic anticoagulation are quite different. At these adjusted concentrations which produce equivalent anticoagulation, each of these inhibitors produces a different level of inhibition of thrombin generation. At the same level of anticoagulation, these three FDA-approved anticoagulants produce different degrees of inhibition in terms of the generation of thrombin-antithrombin complex (fig. 3) and prothrombin fragment $F_{1.2}$ (fig. 4). Similarly, each of these drugs produces prolongation of the ACT for PCI to 300 s at different concentrations, as shown in figure 5. These pharmacokinetic and pharmacodynamic differences clearly indicate that each of these thrombin inhibitors is a distinct drug regardless of potency equivalence in clot-based or amidolytic assays.

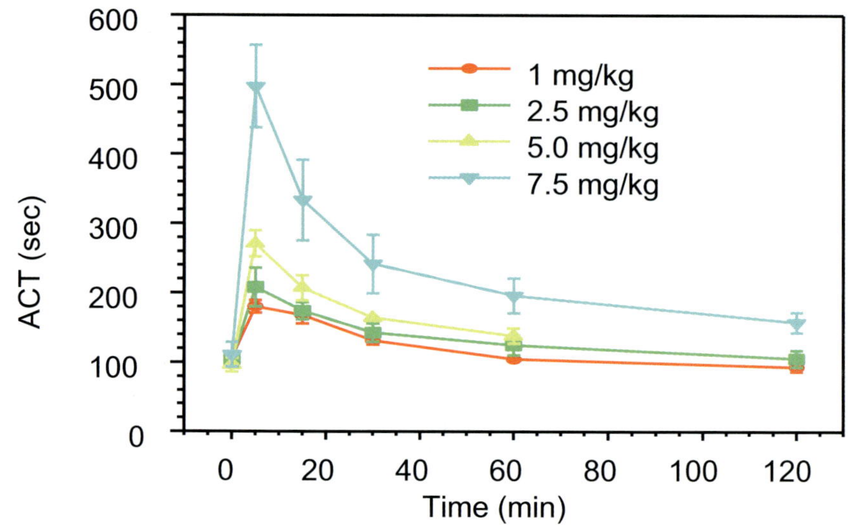

Fig. 6. Pharmacodynamics of various dosages of argatroban in primates as measured by the ACT. Because of the short half-life, a bolus followed by continuous infusion may be an optimal clinical approach.

What Are Some of the Advantages of Argatroban as an Anticoagulant Agent over Other Antithrombin Agents?

Argatroban has several advantages over approved anticoagulant drugs such as heparins and hirudins. Firstly, argatroban does not require antithrombin for its anticoagulant actions. Secondly, it does not have the potential to cross-react with the heparin antibody. Thirdly, because of its short half-life, the effect of argatroban is readily reversible by discontinuation. These comparisons are in reference to heparin. These properties are also shared by other antithrombin agents such as hirudin. However, hirudin is a potent slowly reversible thrombin inhibitor that can compromise the biologic and regulatory effects of thrombin. Furthermore, hirudin can produce antibodies that can markedly influence its half-life. Thus, argatroban offers not only certain advantages over heparins but also over other thrombin inhibitors. Additional clinical trials are needed to demonstrate some of these differences.

How Is the Effect of Argatroban Monitored?

Monitoring of argatroban is required to optimize its usage. For therapeutic anticoagulation, monitoring is useful to maintain a steady concentration, particularly in patients with compromised renal and liver functions. In medical patients the aPTT is useful for therapeutic monitoring, however in studies in PCI, argatroban has been monitored by using the ACT. Figure 6 shows the effect of argatroban on the celite ACT after intravenous administration to primates. Dose-proportional increase in the celite ACT was observed. This suggests that the ACT is a reliable method for monitoring the anticoagulant effects of argatroban. The dosage selection of a 325 μg/kg bolus followed by a 25 μg/kg/min infusion was capable of maintaining the ACT at 300–400 s. Proportionate prolongation of the ecarin clotting time (ECT) can also be seen (fig. 7). Both ACT and ECT are proportionate to the circulating argatroban levels in patients undergoing PCI [29, 30]. Based on these types of studies, PCI studies were carried out using argatroban at this dose. Of course, the influence of antiplatelet drugs in combination has to be investigated. The ACT provided a reliable guideline for achieving interventional anticoagulation.

Argatroban may also be effective in anticoagulation in patients undergoing bypass surgery. Of course, the dosage has to be optimized. A 500 μg/kg bolus, followed by a 50 μg/kg/min infusion, may be suggested. Such dosing provides ACT levels in the range of 500–750 s.

In the Event of Argatroban Overdose, How Do We Neutralize the Anticoagulant and Bleeding Effects of Argatroban?

At the present time, there is no specific antidote for argatroban. In the event of an overdose of argatroban or in a patient with compromised clearance, argatroban's anticoagulant effects could theoretically be neutralized by the following methods: (1) hemofiltration or hemodialy-

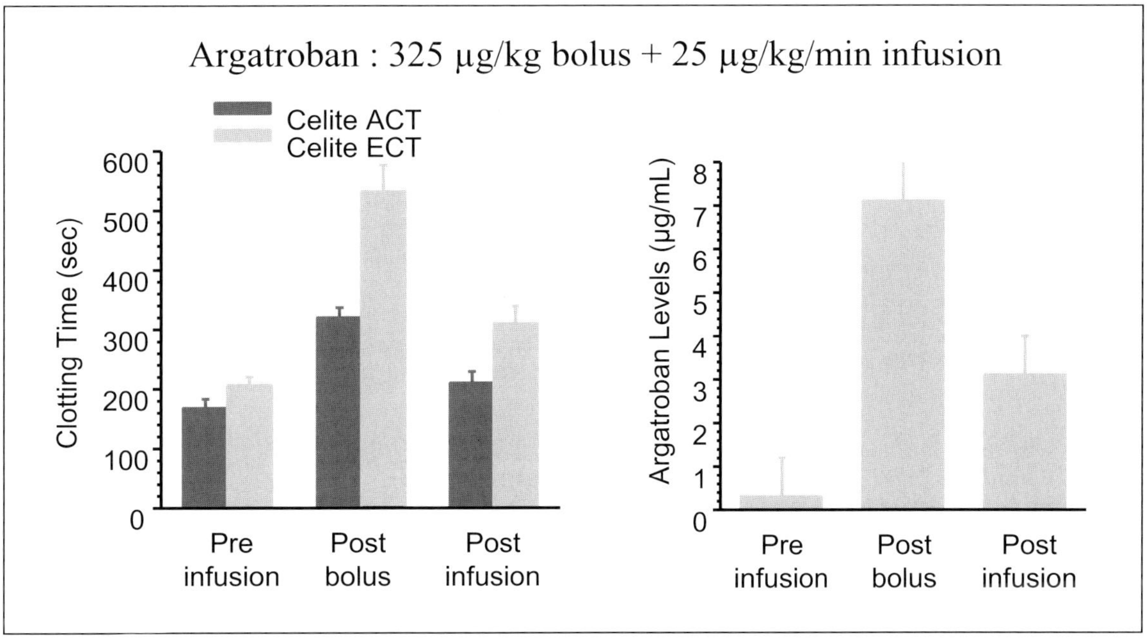

Fig. 7. ACT, celite ECT and absolute levels of argatroban in patients undergoing angioplasty and in patients undergoing percutaneous intervention. The circulating levels of argatroban are proportional to the prolongation of ACT.

sis; (2) plasmapheresis; (3) by treating patients with activated factor VII or prothrombin complex concentrate.

Other routine hemostatic measures can also be implemented.

Are All of the Clinical Effects of Argatroban Dependent on the Inhibition of Thrombin?

Although argatroban is primarily a direct thrombin inhibitor, the therapeutic impact of other potential actions of the molecule warrants further investigation. Argatroban is capable of producing several other effects on the hemostatic and vascular systems. This may or may not be dependent of the inhibition of thrombin. Argatrovan is able to produce the inhibition of platelet activation. As shown in figure 8, argatroban strongly inhibited the thromboplastin-induced activation of platelets as measured by flow cytometry. P-selectin expression is strongly inhibited by argatroban. Argatroban is also capable of inhibiting the contraction of a rat aortic strip induced by endothelin I, as shown in figure 9. The exact mechanism by which this inhibition takes place is not known. However, a dose-dependent effect is quite clear. This indicates that argatroban may also modulate the vascular tone. As argatroban is an arginomimetic drug, it may have additional interactions with cellular and subendothelial sites.

Do We Expect to Observe the Same Drug Interactions with Argatroban and Antiplatelet Agents as Those Observed with Heparin and Antiplatelet Drugs?

The interactions between heparin and antiplatelet drugs are rather complex. However, both argatroban and heparin are antithrombin agents which can modulate platelet function. Unlike heparin, argatroban does not release tissue factor pathway inhibitor (TFPI) and other mediators from the vascular site. Furthermore, argatroban does not cause any mobilization of platelet factor 4. Thus, the interaction between argatroban and antiplatelet drugs may be different in comparison to heparin and may merit further investigation.

Does Argatroban Treatment Lead to the Generation of Antibodies?

Argatroban treatment does not result in the generation of antibodies. This is in contrast to hirudin and hirulog, which are capable of generating these antibodies. These antibodies can seriously alter the treatment management. Argatroban is not a protein and its molecular weight is relatively low, thus it is unlikely that its use will result in the generation of antibodies [28].

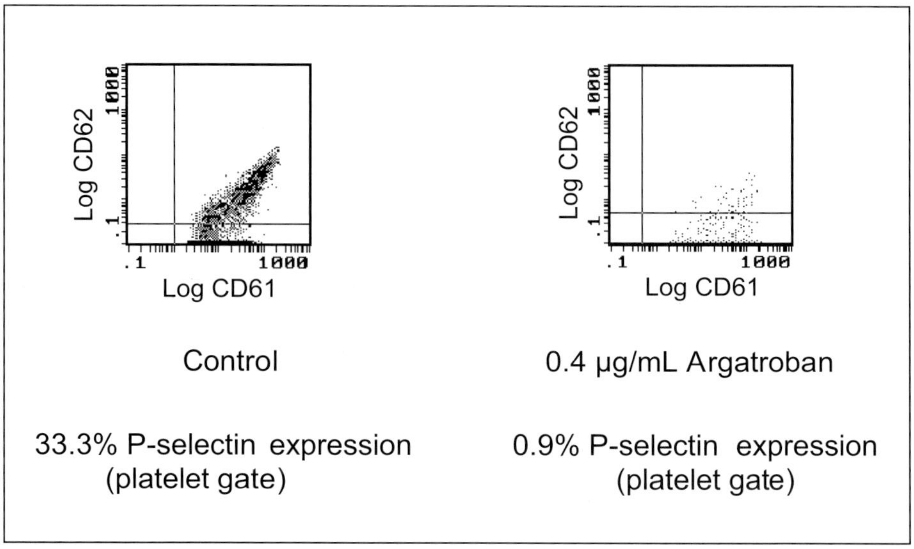

Fig. 8. Argatroban-mediated inhibition of platelet activation as measured by a flow cytometric method. Argatroban produced inhibition of platelet activation.

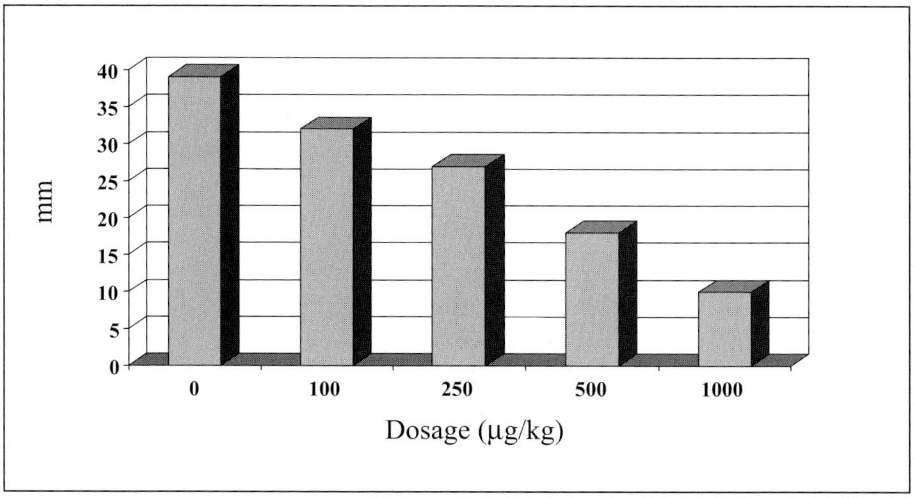

Fig. 9. Effect of argatroban on the endothelin-mediated contraction of rat aortic strip.

Can Argatroban Be Used in Pediatric Patients?

Argatroban is not approved for use in pediatric patients; however, with further study, it may be possible to use argatroban in this setting. It may be a relatively safer drug in comparison to heparin and hirudin.

Both heparin and hirudin have a relatively narrower therapeutic window than argatroban. Dose adjustment may be needed with argatroban for specific indications in pediatric patients.

Can Argatroban Be Used in Pregnant and Nursing Women?

Teratology studies have been performed in rats with intravenous doses up to 27 mg/kg/day (0.3 times the recommended maximum human dose based on body surface area) and rabbits at intravenous doses up to 10.8 mg/kg/day (0.2 times the recommended maximum human dose based on body surface area) and have revealed no evidence of impaired fertility or harm to the fetus due to argatroban.

There are, however, no adequate and well-controlled studies in pregnant women. Because animal reproduction studies are not always predictive of human response, this drug should be used during pregnancy only if clearly needed.

It is not known whether this drug is excreted in human milk. Because many drugs are excreted in human milk and because of the potential for serious adverse reactions in nursing infants from argatroban, a decision should be made whether to discontinue nursing or to discontinue

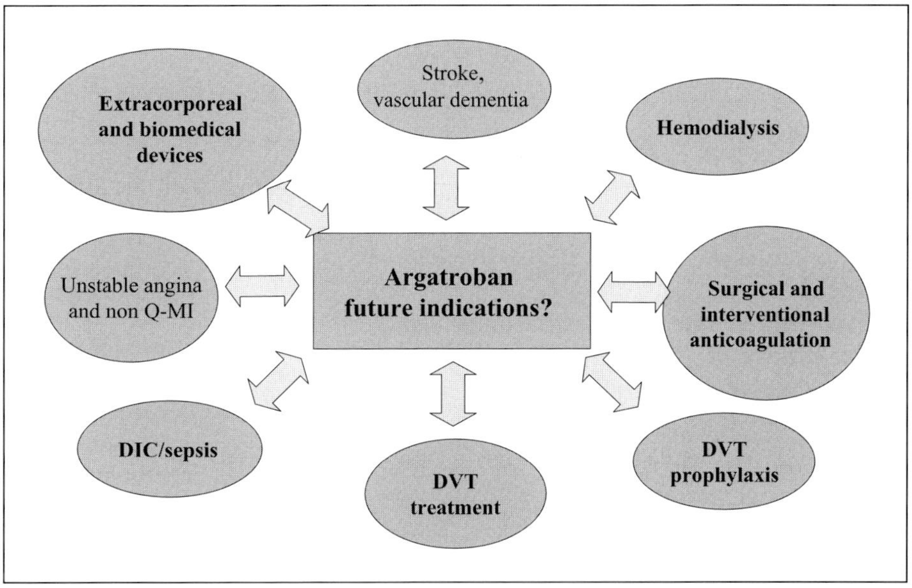

Fig. 10. Possible future indications for argatroban. Although approved in specific indications, argatroban can readily be used in all of the intravenous indications where heparin is used.

the drug, taking into account the importance of the drug to the mother.

What May Be Future Indications for Argatroban?

Currently, argatroban has been developed as an anticoagulant drug. In acute indications, argatroban may turn out to be a better drug than heparin because of its pharmacologic profile. Figure 10 lists some of the possible future indications in which argatroban may be used. In heparin- and hirudin-compromised patients, argatroban may be effectively utilized as an anticoagulant drug. Argatroban may be used as an anticoagulant with biomedical devices. Hemodilution and other factors will not alter its action since the actions of argatroban are not dependent on antithrombin (AT). This agent may be used in hemodialysis; however, with a high flux machine, it is conceivable that some of the argatroban could be lost.

The FDA has recently approved the use of argatroban in PCI in HIT patients. Certainly, this agent may be used in non-HIT patients as well. As argatroban has proven efficacious in PCI, it is possible that at a 50% increased dosage, it could be used in surgical coronary artery bypass graft (CABG). Argatroban may be useful in acute coronary syndromes. Thus, it may find expanded indications in various thrombotic and cardiovascular conditions.

Argatroban may have a specific use in off-pump cardiopulmonary bypass surgery. At relatively low dosages, this drug can be optimized for this indication. Because of its direct anticoagulant effect and relatively simpler structure, argatroban may be useful as a topical and local anticoagulant. Since hemodilution and hemoconcentration do not alter its anticoagulant actions, argatroban may be useful in adjunctive management of cancer and cancer-associated thrombosis. It may be the drug of choice for adjunct medication with antiplatelet and thrombolytic drugs. Argatroban could also be developed for surface coating of devices and stents. Because of its direct anticoagulant actions, it may be better than heparin. It can also be used for organ/cellular preservation. Argatroban has shown some antiinflammatory actions and as such could be developed as an antiproliferative agent.

What Are Some of the Unresolved Issues in the Development of Argatroban?

There are several unresolved issues in the development of argatroban as an anticoagulant, antithrombotic and antiischemic drug. Additional clinical trials are needed to demonstrate the antithrombotic and antiischemic effects of argatroban. Despite the profile of this drug and its usefulness in various indications, some of these developmental considerations remain unanswered at this time. Some of these are listed below:

(1) Effective and rapid reversal of the anticoagulant and potential bleeding effects of argatroban.

(2) Treatment of argatroban overdose.

(3) Safety with regard to passage across placental and blood brain barriers.

(4) Effect of long-term usage of argatroban in specific indications.

(5) Monitoring issues for argatroban dosing and the selection of a suitable method.

(6) Concomitant use of argatroban with other drugs.

(7) Clinical validation of argatroban in specific indications in pediatrics.

(8) Elucidation of the additional mechanisms of action of argatroban.

(9) Effect of argatroban on the auto-regulatory process for the control of anticoagulation.

(10) Dosage optimization for specific groups of patients.

Argatroban is an anticoagulant drug which has been in clinical use for almost 11 years, with an acceptable safety and efficacy profile. Argatroban has been approved in the US for therapeutic and medical anticoagulation in heparin-compromised patients. If, in fact, this anticoagulant is useful in HIT patients, its efficacy may be comparable or better in non-HIT patients requiring anticoagulation. Therefore, it is important to develop this drug for wider use. It is likely that argatroban will prove to be efficacious in many of the indications where heparin is used intravenously. It is, however, important to know that there are basic differences between heparin and argatroban.

Since its introduction in the US, argatroban has been well accepted and it is likely to find additional clinical indications. With additional validation in specific clinical trials, this drug will make a major impact on the treatment of arterial and venous thrombosis.

Acknowledgements

The authors are highly indebted to Professor Okamoto, who has been the main inspiring individual in the continuing work on investigations into argatroban. This drug has provided a unique challenge to all of us and we will continue to probe the polypharmacologic action and endogenous interactions of this unique drug. A man of great vision and insight, Professor Okamoto's teachings will have a profound impact on our understanding of thrombosis and its management.

References

1 Fareed J, Lewis BE, Callas D, Hoppensteadt DA, Walenga JM, Bick RL: Antithrombin agents: The new class of anticoagulant and antithrombotic drugs. Clin Appl Thromb Hemost 1999;5(suppl 1):S45–S55.

2 Fareed J, Hoppensteadt DA, Bacher P, Messmore HL: Antithrombin agents: The new class of antithrombotic drugs; in Pifarre R, Scanlon PJ (eds): Evidence-Based Management of Acute Coronary Syndrome. Philadelphia, Hanley & Belfus, 2001, pp 131–146.

3 Fareed J, Callas D, Hoppensteadt DA, Lewis BE, Bick RL, Walenga JM: Antithrombin agents as anticoagulants and antithrombotics: Implications in drug development. Semin Hematol 1999;36:42–56.

4 Fareed J, Callas D, Hoppensteadt D, Jeske W, Walenga JM: Recent developments in antithrombotic agents. Exp Opin Invest Drugs 1995;4:389–412.

5 Fareed J, Hoppensteadt DA, Breddin HK: Current perspectives in antithrombotic therapy. Hämostaseologie 2001;21:78–85.

6 Fareed J, Hoppensteadt DA: Antithrombin and anti-Xa agents in the control of thrombogenesis. Pharmazie 2001:56(suppl 1):S12–S21.

7 Jeske W, Walenga JM, Lewis BE, Fareed J: Pharmacology of argatroban. Exp Opin Invest Drugs 1999;8:625–654.

8 Kaiser B, Callas D, Walenga JM, Fareed J: Synthetic and recombinant antithrombin drugs. Exp Opin Invest Drugs 1998;7:963–985.

9 Lewis BE, Wallis DE, Berkowitz SD, Matthai WH, Fareed J, Walenga JM, Bartholomew J, Sham R, Lerner RG, Zeigler ZR, Rustagi PK, Jang IK, Rifkin SD, Moran J, Hursting MJ, Kelton JG, for the ARG-911 Study Investigators: Argatroban anticoagulant therapy in patients with heparin-induced thrombocytopenia. Circulation 2001;103:1838–1843.

10 Lewis BE, Ferguson JJ, Grassman ED, Fareed J, Walenga JM, Joffrion J, Wrona L, Johnson SA, Schwarz RP, McKiernan T: Successful coronary interventions performed with argatroban anticoagulation in patients with heparin-induced thrombocytopenia and thrombosis syndrome. J Invasive Cardiol 1996;8:410–417.

11 Topol EJ, Bonan R, Jewitt D, Sigwart U, Kakkar VV, Rothman M, de Bono D, Ferguson J, Willerson JT, Strony J, Ganz P, et al: Use of a direct antithrombin, hirulog, in place of heparin during coronary angioplasty. Circulation 1993;87:1622–1629.

12 Zawilska K, Zozulinska M, Turowiecka Z, Blahut M, Drobnik L, Vinazzer H: The effect of a long-acting recombinant hirudin (PEG-hirudin) on experimental disseminated intravascular coagulation (DIC) in rabbits. Thromb Res 1993;69:315–320.

13 Sakata Y, Curriden S, Lawrence D, Griffin JH, Loskutoff DJ: Activated protein C stimulates the fibrinolytic activity of cultured endothelial cells and decreases antiactivator activity. Proc Natl Acad Sci USA 1985;82:1121–1125.

14 De Fouw NJ, van Hinsberg VW, de Jong YF, Haverkate F, Bertina RM: The interaction of activated protein C and thrombin with the plasminogen activator inhibitor released from human endothelial cells. Thromb Haemost 1987;57:176–182.

15 Dichek D, Quertermous T: Thrombin regulation of mRNA levels of tissue plasminogen activator inhibitor-1 in cultured human umbilical vein endothelial cells. Blood 1989;74:222–228.

16 Collen D, Lijnen HR, Todd PA, Goa KL: Tissue-type plasminogen activator: A review of its pharmacology and therapeutic use as a thrombolytic agent. Drugs 1989;38:346–388.

17 Hoylaerts M, Rijken D, Lijnen HR, Collen D: Kinetics of the activation of plasminogen by human tissue plasminogen activator. Role of fibrin. J Biol Chem 1982;257:2912–2919.

18 Coleman RW: Activation of plasminogen by human plasma kallikrein. Biochem Biophys Res Commun 1968;35:273–279.

19 Goldsmith GH, Saito H, Ratnoff OD: The activation of plasminogen by Hageman factor fragments. J Clin Invest 1978;62:54–60.

20 Barabas E, Szell E, Bajusz S: Screening for fibrinolysis inhibitory effect of synthetic thrombin inhibitors. Blood Coagul Fibrinolysis 1993;4:243–248.

21 Callas D, Bacher P, Iqbal O, Hoppensteadt D, Fareed J: Fibrinolytic compromise by simultaneous administration of site-directed inhibitors of thrombin. Thromb Res 1994;74:193–205.

22 Gilboa N, Villannueva GB, Fenton JW II: Inhibition of fibrinolytic enzymes by thrombin inhibitors. Enzyme 1988;40:144–148.
23 Dodt J, Kohler S, Schmitz T, Wilhelm B: Distinct binding sites of Ala 48-hirudin 1–47 and Ala 48-hirudin 48–65 on α thrombin. J Biol Chem 1990;265:713–718.
24 Petersen TE, Roberts HR, Sottrup-Jensen L, Magnusson S: Primary structure of hirudin, a thrombin-specific inhibitor; in Peters H (ed): Peptides of the Biological Fluids. Oxford, Pergamon, 1976, pp 145–149.
25 Scharf M, Engels J, Tripier D: Primary structures of new 'isohirudins'. FEBS Lett 1989;225: 105–110.
26 Okamoto S, Hijikata A, Kikumoto R, Tonomura S, Hara H, Ninomiya K, Maruyama A, Sugano M, Tamao Y: Potent inhibition of thrombin by the newly synthesized derivative No. 805. The importance of stereo structure of its hydrophobic carboxamide portion. Biochem Biophys Res Commun 1981;101:440–446.
27 Walenga JM, Jeske WP, Wood JJ, Ahmad S, Lewis BE, Bakhos M: Laboratory tests for heparin-induced thrombocytopenia: A multicenter study. Semin Hematol 1999;36(suppl 1):22–28.
28 Walenga JM, Ahmad S, Hoppensteadt D, Iqbal O, Hursting MJ, Lewis BE: Argatroban therapy does not generate antibodies that alter its anticoagulant activity in patients with heparin-induced thrombocytopenia. Thromb Res 2002; 105:401–405.
29 Ahmad S, Ahsan A, Iqbal O, Hoppensteadt DA, Lewis BE, Walenga JM, Fareed J: Pharmacokinetics and pharmacodynamics of argatroban as studied by HPLC and functional methods: Implications in the monitoring and dosage-optimizations in cardiovascular patients. Clin Appl Thromb Hemost 1998;4:243–249.
30 Callas D, Fareed J: Comparative anticoagulant effects of various thrombin inhibitors, as determined in the ecarin clotting time method. Thromb Res 1996;83:463–468.

Pathophysiology of Haemostasis and Thrombosis

Author Index Vol. 32, Suppl. 3, 2002

Subject Index Vol. 32, Suppl. 3, 2002

KARGER
Fax +41 61 306 12 34
E-Mail karger@karger.ch
www.karger.com

Accessible online at:
www.karger.com/pht

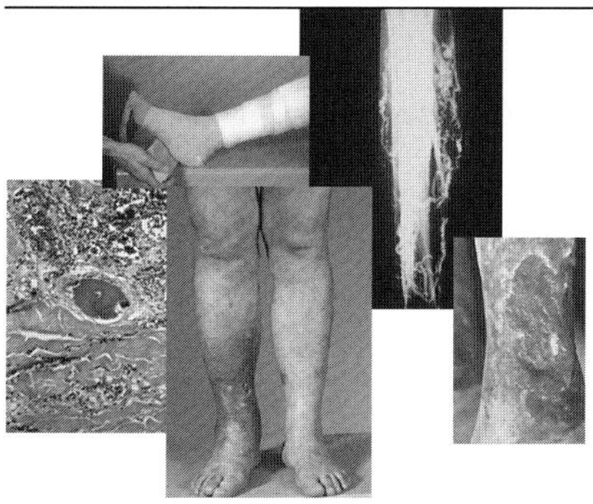

An update on all aspects in ...

Management of Leg Ulcers

Editors: J. Hafner, A.-A. Ramelet, W. Schmeller, U.V. Brunner

Chronic leg ulcers affect approximalety 1% of the adult population in industrial countries. They cause major disability and their enormous socioeconomic impact is still underestimated. This volume provides comprehensive information on the assessment and treatment of leg ulcers.
Different aspects of venous leg ulcers like epidemiology, examination with Doppler and duplex sonography, venography, functional assessments as well as the most common modern classifications are recapitulated. Also, conservative treatment methods such as compression therapy, mobilization of the ankle joint and lymph drainage or different surgical techniques for recalcitrant venous ulcers are discussed.
The chapters dealing with diabetic foot ulcers give a general outlook including patient instruction, orthopedic footwear and podiatric care along with management of the diabetic foot infection, and the indications for orthopedic and vascular interventions.
General practitioners, internists, surgeons, dermatologists, as well as nurses, podiatrists, and physiotherapists will find this publication an indispensable summary on the state of the art in the management of chronic leg ulcers.

Contents

Current Problems in Dermatology, Vol. 27
Series Editor: Burg, G. (Zurich)
ISSN 0070–2064

Management of Leg Ulcers
Editors: Hafner, J. (Zurich); Ramelet, A.-A. (Lausanne); Schmeller, W. (Lubeck); Brunner, U.V. (Zurich)
X + 294 p., 76 fig., 25 in color, 42 tab., hard cover, 1999
CHF 112.– / DEM 134.– / USD 97.50
Prices subject to change
EUR price for Germany, USD price for USA only
ISBN 3–8055–6654–9

Fields of Interest: Dermatology; Phlebology, Angiology, Internal Medicine, Gerontology

KI 99479

KARGER

Journal Publication

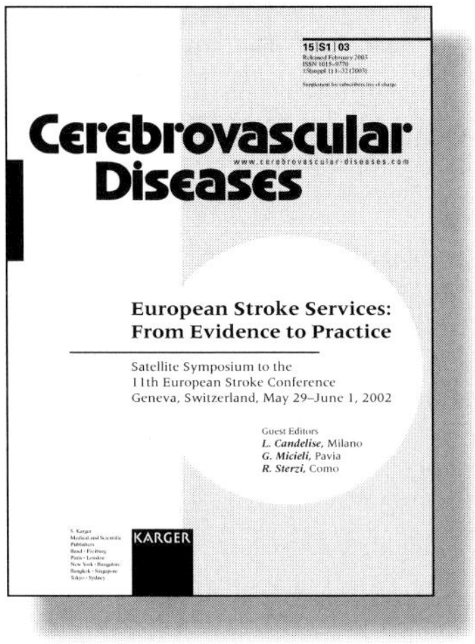

European Stroke Services: From Evidence to Practice

Editors
Livia Candelise
Giuseppe Micieli
Roberto Sterzi

Neurology

Contents

www.karger.com/ced

KI 03417

Cerebrovascular Diseases
Editors: Bogousslavsky, J. (Lausanne), Hennerici, M.G. (Mannheim)
ISSN 1015–9770
Special issue: Vol. 15, Suppl. 1 (2003)
Included in subscription

European Stroke Services: From Evidence to Practice
Satellite Symposium to the 11th European Stroke Conference, Geneva, May–June 2002
Editors: Candelise, L. (Milano); Micieli, G. (Pavia); Sterzi, R. (Como)
IV + 32 p., 6 fig., 5 tab., soft cover, 2003
CHF 29.– / EUR 20.50 / USD 25.25
Prices subject to change
EUR price for Germany, USD price for USA only
ISBN 3–8055–7553–X

KARGER

Order Form

Please send: ____ copy/ies

Postage and handling free with prepayment

Payment:
☐ Check enclosed ☐ Please bill me

Please charge to my credit card
☐ American Express ☐ Diners ☐ Eurocard
☐ MasterCard ☐ Visa

Card No.: ____________________

Exp. date: ____________________

Orders may be placed with any bookshop, subscription agency, directly with the publisher or through a Karger distributor.

Fax: +41 61 306 12 34
S. Karger AG, P.O. Box, CH–4009 Basel (Switzerland)
E-Mail karger@karger.ch, **www.karger.com**

Name/Address: ____________________

Date: ____________________

Signature: ____________________